THE POWER OF LOVE

Sequel to The Girl with the Emerald Brooch
1965 – 1981

Jacqueline Creek

Enjoy the Book
Jacqueline Creek

J. R. Nicholls

First Published in 2017
by J R Nicholls
Denby Dale

Editing by Anne Grange at Wild Rosemary Writing Services
Text Copyright © Jacqueline Creek 2017
Cover photograph courtesy of Sheffield City Council

ISBN: 978-1-911347-07-1

1 3 5 7 9 10 8 6 4 2

Printed and bound in Great Britain by
D&M Heritage Press, Huddersfield HD4 7BH

Praise for Jackie's first book, 'The Girl with the Emerald Brooch'

'A compelling read'... John Irvine Clarke – Author and Poet.

'The heart of it'... Julie Mellor – Poet

'Heartwarming and heart-wrenching in equal measure'... Amazon Customer

'Great Memories and Great detail'... Roy Turton

'You will love this book. Life in the fifties and sixties'... Sandra P

'So well written you feel you are with her throughout'... S. Cleary

'A gripping read a page turner with laughs and tears'... Sarah Bennet

'I really enjoyed her honesty'... Amazon Customer

'Excellent read, I like the way she writes'... Shert.bert

'What an amazing woman, an absolutely fantastic read'... Amazon Customer

'Fantastic. A must read!!!'... Amazon Customer

'A book for all ages, a great book'... Danielle Spencer

Acknowledgements

To John and Dave with love

Thanks to all who made this story possible.

1: 1975

Warm needles of light sought my closed eyes, as the long rays from the Mediterranean sun pierced the ventilation holes in the metal shutters. I looked around in the semi-darkness. The crumpled top sheet lay beside the bed on the tiled floor, the room heady with the scent of sex. The creased and damp bottom sheet clung to me as I turned towards him, still in the depths of sleep. Sensing movement, he reached out. Unable to resist, I folded myself into his arms. Within seconds, his growing erection pulsed against my skin.

I had no need of foreplay; he had pleasured me enough throughout the night. I needed him: his touch, his weight, his scent, his warmth. With him, I unveiled a passion I never knew my body possessed. I pulled him onto me.

'Fill me.'

~

I awoke for the second time that morning. The usual all-consuming guilt washed over me as my thoughts turned to John, back home.

Someone knocked on the door. 'Servicio en la habitación.'

'Just a minute,' I replied.

'Dave, the cleaner is here, time to get up.' I shook his shoulder.

He pulled me towards him again.

'No, not now.'

He grinned and tugged my hand. 'She'll come back.'

I pulled free and ran into the shower, turned it on, and stood beneath the spray of warm water.

1

'You don't think that's going to stop me, do you?' he said, as he pulled the shower curtain back and joined me. My heart missed a beat and the familiar thrill filled my body.

'Stop it, Dave; she'll be back in a minute.'

The broad grin spread across his face.

'Dave, I'm serious.' I laughed.

'So am I,' he said, and pressed me against the wall.

'Dave…' His mouth covered mine as he lifted me onto him. The water sprayed and trickled between us.

~

We were staying in the Hotel Belvedere. It was our last day in Majorca before going home. I had promised John I would finish the affair with Dave while I was away. Yet, here we were, walking from the hotel, hand-in-hand, like any other couple deeply in love.

I was wearing a long, pale ivory cheesecloth skirt, a long-sleeved matching top with a draw-cord neckline, six rows of beads I had bought from the hippy market, cork wedge heel sandals with corded ankle ties, and a long fine headband scarf with the ends trailing down my back. The headband was embellished with small silk flowers. My hair was long and painfully straightened. Dave wore his wide-legged flares, an open necked cotton T shirt and a suede waistcoat. With his platform shoes, his six-foot-two frame accelerated to six-five. We had loved and played all week like a couple of exuberant teenagers, unlike civilised adults now into their thirties.

Passing rows of red and purple climbing bougainvillea, clinging to everything in its path, we stopped at a beach café for a beer and a glass of wine. As the day turned to evening, the changing shades of the setting sun bathed everything in shades of gold. Finishing our drinks, we removed our shoes and walked along the edge of the sea as it lapped onto the beach. We hardly spoke. What more could be said? Finishing with Dave would break my heart. Yet I owed it to John.

We put on our shoes and made our way to Tito's nightclub. The meal was typical touristy Spanish fare. Dry bread rolls, gazpacho soup, oily chicken and vegetables smothered in greasy gravy, followed by a slice of cake, probably made from leftover bread and sweetened with honey or sugar. The wine was okay though.

We sat with our drinks, holding hands and watched the entertainment – a juggler, a xylophonist and a comedian who told the same jokes in four different languages. The singer and band were good and we took advantage of the dance floor. I looked at the other couples: some waltzing professionally, holding their partners in perfect positions; others like Dave and I, holding each other closely, moving slightly, swaying to the strains of Scott McKenzie's 'Let's go to San Francisco', 'Hang on in There, Baby' by Johnny Bristol, and 'Can't Get Enough of Your Love, Baby' by Barry White.

I placed my head on his chest. The week had passed so quickly and these last few precious hours would not be relived. A sob came up in my throat and my eyes filled with tears. I looked up at him and knew he was thinking the same. His roguish grin, which had first attracted me to him, had vanished. He saw my tears and his chin quivered. It didn't matter who saw.

I looked around; strangers, with their own emotions to contend with. I thought of the war films I had seen, with the women dancing with their husbands or lovers, wondering if that would be their last time together.

~

The airport was hot and crowded; coaches and taxis contesting for space. Frustrated drivers pressed their horns. We made our way into the terminal. Neither of us spoke.

Joining the check-in queue, we presented our flight tickets and handed over our cases; then made our way to Passport Control, where our passports were dutifully stamped. Entering the departure lounge, frustrated people fanned themselves with newspapers and magazines, while the knowledgeable Spanish women carried fans. We managed to find a quiet area and sat down.

Dave spoke first. 'Is that it, then, it's over?' He didn't look at me. He stared out of the window, watching the planes taking off and landing.

3

I took a deep breath.

'Dave, you know it has to be, there's no alternative.' I shook my head and clasped my hands. 'I can't put John through any more, I've hurt him enough. He loves me and…'

Dave's fiery passion welled up inside him and he turned and grabbed hold of my arms.

'I love you, Jack.' His eyes were dark with passion and anger.

'I know, Dave, I love you, you know that, but I'm married to John and have been for ten years.'

He took his hands from my arms and burst into tears; great heaving sobs.

'I can't live without you in my life, Jack.' His tanned face contorted with pleading.

'Stop it, Dave, I'm not enjoying this either. It's a wrench for me too.'

The public address system announced our flight. A shuttle bus transported us to the plane, standing in the distance on the melting tarmac. Service personnel were busy in the blistering heat beneath its undercarriage. Waiting in turn, we climbed the steps and silently boarded the Boeing 737.

We fastened our seatbelts and listened to the safety demo. The doors were locked and cross-checked. Dave sat nearest the window, I was in the centre seat; the seat on my other side was unoccupied. As we taxied slowly towards the runway, the Captain informed us we were in a queue for take-off. After ten minutes, the plane swung onto the head of the runway and stopped abruptly, engines whining, holding back power.

'Are you okay?' asked Dave as he took hold of my hand.

I gave it a squeeze. 'Hmm…' I nodded.

There was a short silence. The passengers were subdued. Then the roar from the engines became louder, the cabin began to vibrate and the plane pushed forward. Gently and then with increasing force and accelerating speed, it left the ground. The land tilted sharply beneath us as the wheels stowed into the undercarriage.

4

The stewardesses remained seated as the plane tilted and banked to the left, still climbing; then levelled before the engine noise faded and the plane settled into a cruise. Twenty minutes later, the sounds of seat belts unfastening and drinks trolleys filled the cabin. I sat back, closed my eyes and wondered why I had allowed our relationship to go this far.

2: Ten years earlier

It was Tuesday before John and I could get away on our honeymoon. I was over the worst of my bronchitis. We left Sheffield on Tuesday morning at seven o'clock, after John had filled the tank with petrol the night before. I had moaned at the cost of petrol. Five pounds it cost to fill the tank.

'It will get us down to Torquay and most of the way back,' he had said. I still thought it was a lot of money, yet I was glad that he'd managed to get double Green Shield stamps. I was saving them for a pop-up toaster.

It took an hour to get to Chesterfield and over an hour to reach Derby; the same to Birmingham. We drove to Worcester and Gloucester, passing quaint towns and villages, Bristol and the Clifton suspension bridge. I had never been this far south before. It was so exciting. As we drove through the Cheddar Gorge, I noticed the lush green grass and strange red soil.

We pulled into a lay-by to eat our sandwiches, and drank a flask of lukewarm tea. Afterwards, getting out of the car, I picked a handful of the peculiar red soil and rubbed it between my fingers, leaving red stains across my palms. I couldn't understand why it wasn't black like northern soil.

We journeyed on, through Bridgewater, Taunton and Exeter. My map reading continued. The road signs for Torquay soon came into view and we left the A38, drove through Newton Abbot and finally arrived at half past three. We had done well: there had hardly been any traffic on the roads, stopping once for toilets and the lay-by in the

Cheddar Gorge, and for red traffic lights at all the towns we passed through.

John parked the car and we walked for a while to stretch our legs. The view was beautiful. Boats and yachts bobbed in the harbour. The sea was blue and smooth as silk, unlike the rough grey North Sea. Grassy plains tumbled down to the golden sands. I wondered what Mum and Dad would think of this. I couldn't wait to send a postcard home to show them.

As we walked, we noticed the expensive prices in the shops. Getting back into the car, we drove around the streets for a while, looking for B&Bs. There was nothing under seventeen shillings and sixpence a night. We drove further out and arrived at a place called Babbacombe, which looked very quaint and the rates were fifteen shillings. We chose a welcoming little place on a side street.

'Excuse me asking, do you have any cats? My husband has an allergy to them.'

She gave a warm smile. 'No, no cats or dogs. Anything else I can help you with?'

'In that case, we'd like a double room until Saturday, please,' I said.

'Of course, do come in. Mrs Mannish is my name – it is a bit of a mouthful, so call me Pat,' she said as she led us upstairs.

I didn't hesitate in letting her see my wedding ring. 'This is the first time we've been anywhere since getting married last Saturday,' I said.

'Oh! You are on honeymoon, how lovely. Congratulations.' She was just about to unlock a door when she hesitated. 'No, come with me, I have something better, and no one is coming in until the weekend. You did say you were leaving on Saturday, didn't you?'

She took us up to the attic, which had a small dormer window. 'If you look to the right, you can see the sea and Shag Rock.'

I went over to the window, stood on my tiptoes, peered to the right and looked out.

'That's marvellous. Come and look, John.' I beckoned him over.

'There's a wash basin in this room and the bathroom and W.C. is on the floor below,' said Pat, who handed over the key. 'There are some information leaflets and What's On guides on the hall table, help yourselves – some of them have free admission. Dinner's at five-thirty and breakfast at nine.'

~

The next few days were the happiest ever. The sun shone and we sunbathed in grassy areas just off the coastal path and discussed how the people down here spoke with a different dialect and what made the soil red. John said it was because of all the previous battles fought in the south. I was taking it all in until he laughed. We paddled in the sea at Oddicombe, picnicked in Ansteys Cove and visited Cockington with its thatched roof cottages. I took photographs with our Kodak 127 Brownie camera. Mum and Dad would want to see the places we'd been to.

The places we visited were like the pictures on top of biscuit tins and chocolate boxes. Who lived in these places? How could anyone afford to live in such beautiful areas? We drove back to Babbacombe. I had to find out. I wanted to live where the air was pure and the sea was blue and our children would sleep without drop-forge hammers thundering through the night. Mum and Dad could come too and Dad's chest would be a lot better.

~

Saturday came far too soon and it was time to leave. I walked to the florist after breakfast and bought a few flowers for Pat. I thanked her for making us so welcome and giving us one of her best rooms at no extra charge. We promised to come back next year, and then began our long journey home.

~

As we were tired from traveling, we stayed in my old bed at Mum's, and moved in with John's family the following day. My clothes were packed and the drawers and wardrobe stood empty, apart from my bridesmaid dress which I had worn for Auntie Joy's wedding as a small girl. No doubt Mum would dispose of it. I emptied the chest of drawers except one, which held my bottom drawer collection. Larger wedding presents were carefully placed alongside the items I had painstakingly collected since our engagement. As we wouldn't be in our own home for a while, our presents, and towels, tea towels, a tea set, a biscuit barrel and other precious items, had to remain here.

We returned the white Vauxhall 101 car we had hired for the wedding and traded our old Austin A40 in for £5 towards the cost of a 1961 Morris Oxford estate painted in two shades of blue, paid for from our savings.

~

John's mum was an angel. She insisted I had a hot meal every day when I came home from my day work. No sooner had I washed my hands than a plate of meat and potato pie, or a bowl of stew and dumplings or sausage and mash was placed on the table for me. This was so different from meals at my mum's. Mum had almost stopped cooking as she worked the evening shift, and said there wasn't much point in cooking any more: Jo was away at college, Ian ate school meals and Dad could have a hot meal in the works canteen.

'What about me?' I said. 'I haven't got a canteen to go to.'

'You can manage on a sandwich,' she replied.

'A sandwich? A sandwich? I have sandwiches for lunch. I don't want them for tea as well.'

'You're not helpless, are you? You can get something out of the fridge.'

'Mum, I don't get in till six o'clock, and have to leave an hour later for my other job.'

'Stop making a song and dance about it. Anyway, you always say you can manage on a cup of tea and a cig.'

'Only because I have to…'

She pulled her coat on and stormed out of the house to work.

~

'There's some apple pie and custard for after, Jackie love,' John's mum said.

9

'Thanks, Mabel. I'll be putting on weight at this rate.'

'You can stand it – you could do with a bit more weight on you, love.'

'She'll put enough on when she starts having babies,' said Mary, John's sister, who was having one of her better days.

'You're not ready for that yet, are you, love?' said Mabel, looking at me and then across at Mary. 'They need a bit of time on their own,' she added as she poured my tea.

John and I looked across the table at each other and laughed.

'We'll wait until we've got our own place before we start with a family,' I said.

I loved living there. She took me in and looked after me as if I was one of her own.

~

Back at work at the chemist's the following day, I asked Mr Fox if I could have a couple of hours off to go into Sheffield, as I had an appointment at the family planning clinic.

'Going on the pill, eh?' We were counting out tablets at the time. His cigarette dangled from his bottom lip; mine was in an ashtray.

'I can now I'm married,' I said. I put the tablet bottle down as the phone started to ring. I went to answer it and listened to the customer's query.

'Just a minute,' I said to the caller and went over to Mr Fox. 'It's Mrs Baker. She wants to know if the new medicine she's taking will give her cramp, as she's only had it since she started taking the tablets.'

'I've had a few of these enquiries lately. Tell her I'll phone back when I've looked up her prescription to see what she was prescribed.' He blew the ash off the tablets on the table and continued to count them.

'You'd think the doctors would tell them if there were any side effects, wouldn't you,' I said, as I took another prescription from the in-tray.

'There's too many,' Mr Fox replied. 'And what affects one person, might not another.'

'It gets complicated, doesn't it?'

'Hmm.' He licked the label and stuck it on the bottle. 'What does John think about you going on the pill?'

'He's all for it, obviously.' I wrote *Amitriptyline tabs* on the "wanted" list as I counted out the last of the tablets.

'The Thalidomide events not put you off?' He lit a cigarette and then realised he still had one in his mouth.

The shop doorbell rang.

'Yes and no,' I said as I went to serve, and placed another prescription at the bottom of the in-tray.

~

The visit to the clinic was like the third degree. A vaginal and breast examination; weight and height check; blood pressure reading and a family history questionnaire wasn't enough for these doctors.

'When are you planning to have your first child?'

'How many do you intend having?'

'Have you had an inter-uterine device fitted?'

'What contraception are you using at the moment?'

'What kind of periods do you have?'

'Are they regular?'

I came away with six month's supply of *Gynovlar 21* tablets, and was told to also use other methods of contraception for the first two weeks.

Chapter 3

We were in the Crown one night. It was early on and not many people or workers were in. A couple of men sat at the bar in the taproom, seeing who could make the best tank out of empty cigarette packets.

Some of the steel companies and engineering companies had moved to other areas, so trade had dropped off somewhat. Arnie and Kitty were upstairs and didn't come down till late evening, nowadays.

I was standing on a stool, putting up a display of the new Babycham and Cherry B glasses on the glass shelves at the back of the bar. John was stocking up the bottle shelves. Some directors and managers came in from the brewery.

'Good evening,' they said, as they ordered drinks. 'Is Arnie in?'

'He's upstairs,' said John as he pulled three halves of bitter. 'Is it important?'

'No, I'll catch him tomorrow lunchtime. Get one for you and Jackie,' he added.

'Thanks, Mr Kendall,' I said.

I turned around and continued with the display. John rang the payment through the till and continued wiping the bottles. One of the chaps was new; he'd not been in before. Apparently, he had come over from the Runcorn depot. There had been talk of Stones' being taken over by Bass Charrington, and many meetings had taken place recently.

They were standing at the bar, observing the clarity of the beer, chatting and having a bit of laugh, when the new chap began colouring his conversation with Fs, Cs, and Bs.

'Would you mind not swearing, please?' John said in a quiet voice.

The conversation stopped dead. The man swung around and faced John. His face turned red, eyes full of anger. I could see his reflection in the mirror. He raised his glass. I thought he was going to throw it at John. The rest of the party stood, silent. John, bent down beneath the counter, stood up and stared at the man, who placed his glass on the bar, adjusting the lapels on his Crombie.

'What did you just tell me to do?' he said.

'I asked you to keep your language down. If you want to swear, go in the tap room.' John remained calm.

'You can't tell me what to do. Do you know who I am?' He looked at the rest of his party, unbelieving.

'I don't care who you are at the brewery. Right now, you are a customer using foul language. I don't want to hear it and neither does Jackie.'

The man turned and looked around.

'For heaven's sake, there's no one in.' He saw me. 'Only the barmaid and she'll be used to it.'

'The barmaid happens to be my wife and I don't want you swearing in her presence. Do you swear like that in front of your wife?'

The man's face darkened. He leaned forward.

'I'll have your job for this. I've never been so humiliated in my life.' He looked at his colleagues and walked out. His colleagues glanced at John, frowned and then half-smiled, finished their drinks and followed.

Nothing came of it. Life carried on as normal.

~

We were another few months nearer to getting our flat when I saw an advertisement in a magazine.

'Here, John, what do you think to this…a Rolls Rapide twin tub washing machine and spin dryer?' I showed him the picture.

'Thirty-nine guineas – that's not bad, is it?' he replied.

'It's excellent,' I said. 'Bendix and Hotpoint machines cost a fortune.

'It will fit under the kitchen worktop in the flat and fill from the hot and cold water taps, with a hose, hmm! Might be worth looking into.' John was looking over my shoulder.

'There's a Hire Purchase arrangement as well. Look beneath the picture.'

'Six pound nineteen shillings deposit, followed by one-hundred-and-four payments of eight-shillings and threepence a week – we can manage that,' he said.

'I'm going to fill the form in and send for the free brochure, what do you think?'

Within a month, the new washer was delivered. John's mum was afraid of it, so we took over the family wash.

~

A few weeks later, I had some bad news. Mr Fox told me he was retiring. He had sold the business to a younger couple and as they were both pharmacists, I wouldn't be required. They also had someone in mind to serve in the shop.

I had worked there for seven years and now I was looking for a job.

'The co-op chemist in Hillsborough is advertising for someone,' said John, one night.

'I don't want a job this side of Sheffield, John. When we get the flat, we will be on the south side and I'll not want to travel that far. The same applies if I were to get work over there while I'm living here.'

Kitty, the landlady at the pub came up with a solution.

'Why don't you work here, Jackie, full-time – lunchtimes and evenings?'

I thought about it.

'What about when we move into our flat? I'll want a proper job then, one I trained for,' I replied.

'You've only got a few months to wait now, so this will tide you over.'

'Well, so long as it's not permanent, I'll do it.'

John wasn't too thrilled. He didn't mind the evenings when he was with me, but wasn't too keen on me working the lunchtimes without him. I told him he'd nothing to worry about; I loved him dearly and couldn't wait until we had our own little nest.

~

Our Saturday afternoons were spent travelling to Leeds and queuing to shop in the *Bus Stop* boutique. With their constant supply of the latest London fashions, affordable now we were no longer saving for a house, I became a regular customer. I had my hair cut and styled like Dusty Springfield's or Cilla Black's, although, because of its natural curl, it wouldn't stay straight. I let it grow and thicken up, which resulted in an Afro-Caribbean style like Marsha Hunt's from the musical *Hair*.

Working at the pub full time, I began to get a lot of attention from the opposite sex and found it flattering and enjoyable. In 1966, when the World Cup was on, some of the football matches were played at Hillsborough. It was a very busy two weeks and even the German supporters pestered me for dates. I loved the attention. Offers of drinks, and lifts home after the lunchtime shift came daily from workers and management alike.

Proposals of work came from all sources, as well as a proposal of marriage from one German. I was offered work in a betting shop and secretarial work from two steelworks. A motor mechanic who ran a nearby repair shop, wanted me for reception and office work, and a foundry boss offered a general office duties position. Most of the offers were for the wrong reasons. No one asked if I had any qualifications and some were quite shocked when I told them I was an unqualified pharmacist.

'Ahh, make them ill by night and cure them by day,' said one of the men.

~

I no longer fitted in with my old friends, who now had children, and their talk of babies and teething, which seemed to be their only conversation, bored me.

15

I felt more comfortable in the bar, listening to the men's tales, their jokes and carefree attitude, as they rambled on about the women who didn't understand them. I knew more about the men than their wives did, smiling as I eavesdropped on their whispered conversations and racy jokes. Their secrets, strengths and weaknesses were safe with me. We played darts and talked at length about our favourite football teams and players, and with all the card games my cousin Len had taught me, I was a match for them any day.

~

A Driving School was opening at the top of Mum's street and was advertising for a receptionist. As much as I loved my lunchtimes at the Crown, I wanted the job of receptionist, partly because I preferred full-time work, and because I wanted to learn to drive and it wasn't too far to travel. Two weeks later, I became their receptionist.

My boss was a super guy, always good for a laugh and excellent company. My job entailed making bookings and arranging driving tests, commiserating with clients who failed their tests, and consoling them with tea and biscuits. I celebrated with the ones who passed, and sold them car insurance on a commission basis. Wages and PAYE for the instructors and me was also part of my duties, as well as banking.

I collected greetings cards and gifts for the instructors' wives and girlfriends, and anything else they required, such as keeping important information in the daily log and reminding them when key dates were due. The best part was in between lessons, and when on their breaks, I listened to their tales of the learner drivers.

I asked my boss Barry if he would teach me.

'Not likely,' he replied. 'I won't even teach the wife. Family and friends, no way.'

'I'll take you, Jackie,' said Lyndon, one day. I think he'd been talking to Barry. I wasn't too keen on going with him. He tried it on once too often with me in the back room where I made the tea and sandwiches. However, I did want to learn, so I took him up on his offer.

I told John I'd be late finishing as I was having a lesson after work. At five-thirty, Lyndon finished his break and drove me out towards Rivelin Valley. It was wintertime and the evenings were dark. He turned off up a quiet lane, which is the usual procedure for a first lesson, and we swapped places. As soon as I sat in the driving seat, the back dropped down and I fell back with it. It was something you would see in a *Carry On* film, I began to laugh, thinking I'd caused it to fall. Lyndon took advantage of the situation and because of my laughter, thought his luck was in.

A few years ago I would have been enraged, but I was older now and used to men and their antics.

'Give over Lyndon, I don't fancy you so I'm not going to oblige, let me get up.' I was still half-laughing.

'But Jackie…' His face looked so serious. 'You don't know what effect you have on me.'

'No I don't and don't want to, now help me up.'

'You don't understand…my wife doesn't understand…'

'Oh, here we go, the old wife doesn't understand me routine.'

'Come on, Jackie, it'll not go any further, I promise.'

I stopped laughing.

'Listen to me, Lyndon. Stop this. Now help me up and we'll go back to working together and nothing more will be said. Otherwise…'

Now he seemed concerned. 'You'll not tell Barry, will you?'

'Not if you help me up and take me back.'

He helped me up and repositioned himself, then drove around the streets to pass the time, while telling his tale of woe and the failure of his marriage.

~

'How'd the lesson go?' said John when we returned.

Lyndon looked sheepish as he got out of the car.

'I don't think I'm ready for it yet,' I said, looking at Lyndon.

Lyndon gave a small smile. 'I think she'll make a good driver one day,' he replied. 'It'll take a better man than I to show her.' He winked. 'She'd be better with Barry.'

~

We were still living with John's family when his mum took ill. The lump she hidden beneath her pinny outgrew her body and burst, filling her with septicaemia. She was rushed into hospital for an emergency operation. It was too late. She didn't survive the night.

John's brothers and sisters, along with his dad, made the funeral arrangements while I took over the running of the house and meals.

The undertakers brought her back to the house on the morning of the funeral. She lay in her coffin in front of the window. None of the curtains were closed, unlike Granddad's funeral. Times had changed. The family – her two daughters – Mary and Annie, her three sons, John, Tom and Harry, and her husband, Harry, gathered in the living room, greeting distant relatives with sadness as they arrived. I kept out of the way, in the kitchen, where the kettle boiled continuously.

After providing everyone present with tea or coffee, I moved over to the coffin and looked at her small frame. Doll like, without a smiling pink face and lips, Mabel's face bore the scars of long-time pain. A lovely mother, and with three sons, all with motorbikes, and two teenage girls, must have worried her continuously. I stroked the silver strands of hair and placed my hand over hers, kissed her forehead and thanked her for her son, promising to look after him. I also thanked her for showing me another kind of love and then wept for all her suffering.

~

Living conditions were difficult at first as John and I still had the two jobs. John's dad still worked and so did Tom. Luckily, Harry had since married and moved away. Tom, seeing the difficulties, moved in with his sister Mary, who was also a godsend to me. Although ill, she managed to come up every alternate day, clean the house, and do the food shopping for us. John's dad, who was far stricter than mine, had expected Mabel to be at his disposal, and found it very different with me running the house. I sympathized, but I just couldn't do it all with the two jobs, whereas John was more than willing to help with the chores.

18

Six months later, we were at the top of the housing list for our flat, excitedly checking the post as soon as it arrived, when we had another setback. John's Dad had a severe stroke. After a few weeks in hospital, we found he needed twenty-four hour care. Mary and Annie sought an appropriate care-home for him, where he spent the rest of his days, which were few, as another stroke followed, from which he didn't recover.

John and I were alone. The house was no longer a home and it rang with emptiness. It was lacking people and yet full of memories. Children's laughter echoed from the walls, along with the sound of tearful cries from the owners of gravel-scraped knees. The old black Yorkshire range fireplace, furniture, ornaments and photos were just as John's mum had left them. Who was I to change things? This had been her home; and ours had been getting nearer day by day. Mabel and Harry's children had grown up and left. John, the youngest, would be the last to leave.

Four weeks later, the council officer asked John if he was keeping the tenancy. It wasn't for us; the letter we had been waiting for stood on the mantelpiece. Two weeks later, after thirty years, the keys to the family home were given back to the council for modernising and re-letting.

4

The wait had been worthwhile. At the height of the swinging sixties, we were a trendy couple, with our very own penthouse flat on a council housing development in the Norfolk Park area of Sheffield. It overlooked the park, and the city beyond. Day or night, the views were always spectacular. All for two pounds and ten shillings a week rent.

Brenda and Len's G Plan furniture had been in storage since they emigrated, and now, it fitted in perfectly. The low-level teak sideboard with black legs and matching drop-leaf table, complimented the black leather settee and toning black leather, button-back, G Plan, "Blofeld" winged armchair, which claimed to be the most comfortable chair in the world. We even managed to find a black screen TV.

I papered the feature wall in kingfisher-blue, purple, grey and black abstract wallpaper, and the end wall in a plain textured paper, coloured a lighter shade of blue. The two other walls were windows and I made curtains from plain kingfisher-blue heavy duty Hessian. The long pile carpet was a deep purple wool and nylon mix.

Despite the flat being fabulous, the first year was quite traumatic. John and I rowed over everything and I went back to Mum's.

'Take you back? Not likely. I'll take John in before you,' she said. 'You've made your bed, now lie on it.'

'Mum, it's so difficult working day and night with all the travelling.' I sat at the table, my hands folded beneath my chin. 'It's alright for you, you don't cook anymore. John likes his meals as soon as he finishes work, and even when I do them, he doesn't like this or he doesn't like that.'

'His mum did tell you he was a fussy eater.'

'Yes, I know. That doesn't alter things though, does it? I thought I was fussy, but John takes the biscuit.'

'Time to face the harsh realities of life, Jacqueline.' She looked at me over the top of her glasses, reminding me of Mr Fox. 'The honeymoon's over – time for getting down to the nitty gritty of what makes a marriage work. Wait till the children come along and then you'll know.'

I went back to the flat, defeated. I didn't tell John where I'd been.

~

As the weeks and months followed, I realised that Mum had taught me a lot that day. John and I settled into a more comfortable relationship and we began to feel more like we did before our marriage.

As we adjusted to each other and our differences, life became exciting again and parties followed parties as I made new friends. I left the driving school, as it was too far to travel. Calling upon my knowledge of medicine, I took a job as a telephone order clerk with a wholesale chemist's supplier, and hated it. Not the work itself; it was working with an office full of women.

Having never worked with women before, apart from Doreen at the chemist's when I had first left school, I found them jealous and bitchy. Most of them worked part-time as they had families. The younger full-timers were good fun and we enjoyed each other's company. However, the bitchiness overshadowed everything. Their comments were cruel and heartless, all because I put buying new clothes, make-up and holidays before having children.

'I don't want any yet,' I said. 'There are things to do and places to see – besides, we will be taking over the Crown soon and I don't want to bring a child up in a pub. I don't think it's right.'

'You're just being selfish,' they replied. 'It's your duty to have children.'

'Who says it is? Not in my book,' I'd reply and the arguments would start.

Mum agreed that I should wait a few years and that twenty-eight to twenty-nine would be about right. After all, she'd had me when she was thirty-one, and I was her first.

Even the doctors at the Family Planning Clinic were aggressive regarding the timetables of pregnancies.

'You should be starting your family now,' they said. 'You can't take the "pill" as a permanent contraceptive measure – it's only for use between pregnancies.'

~

At least the younger girls were fun and I started going out with them. John and I changed our nights off at the Crown and I would go with the girls around the town centre pubs and then on to Tiffany's nightclub. John had similar nights out with some lads from his day work, and they finished their evenings in Baileys nightclub.

John didn't like dancing, never had, and it was something I'd missed over the last few years. It was a different type of music nowadays from the Rock and Roll that Hazel, Lynn and I used to dance to. The dance floor bounced as we strutted our stuff to the sounds of Norman Greenbaum with his rendering of 'Spirit in the Sky', and Desmond Dekker with 'Israelites', Thunderclap Newman, Creedence Clearwater Revival and The Rolling Stones. This was a new generation.

I loved the music and the fashions – the wide-bottomed flared trousers, high platform shoes and boots, crop tops and tank tops, and large hooped earrings. The males wore similar clothes, grew their hair long or longer and sported droopy moustaches. It was a new beginning for me and I couldn't get enough of it.

As much as I loved John, I flirted with the men who made advances. I was comfortable in their world. I even went as far as close-dancing with them when the smoochy songs came on. It was exciting. I drew the line at dating though. My heart was with John, despite the fact that he didn't like to dance, was a fussy eater and preferred two wheels to my two legs. He didn't really. I often accused him of that, especially if I was in the mood for more than a cuddle and he would rather watch motor racing or football on TV.

~

It was a Saturday afternoon. John had gone to Bramall Lane to see Sheffield United and I was going to Mum and Dad's, which was now an occasional event, whenever Dad needed his hair cutting.

Getting off the bus at the top of the street, I looked in the window of the butcher's shop, which had recently changed hands. The new owner was a young chap and had given my young brother Ian, an after-school and Saturday job. I watched Ian through the window. He was approaching fifteen, with another year to go before leaving school. He wore a long white overall, almost touching the floor on his skinny body. Ian had taken after me with his build.

A shopper stopped to look in the window. Ian promptly picked up a pig's trotter from the back counter and pulled his hand back up his sleeve so only the trotter was showing. He looked at her and began pointing with the trotter to the different cuts of meat in the window. She laughed and entered the shop. One of Ian's favourite tricks when a shopper came in was to turn towards the back of the shop, and trap a pig's tail in his trouser zip. Making sure his overall was unfastened, he would calmly let his overall ride open while talking to customers. When they noticed the dangling tail, he would look embarrassed and say: 'Oops! Sorry, is my fly undone?'

I walked down Tanfield Road, where I used to live. It was four years since I left, yet it seemed like ages. It was one of many streets in the Owlerton area of Sheffield: rows of smoke-covered red brick terraced houses, side by side, all the same. Only the curtains differed. I thought of our modern flat, just the same — row after row, stacked on top of each other: concrete and steel instead of bricks and mortar.

As it was Saturday, it was quiet. None of the hammers thumped in the surrounding steelworks. The only sound was the occasional cheer from the nearby football ground and the odd dog bark. Children still played outside in the street, girls skipping and hopscotching. Boys with cricket bats and footballs; the metal gates of the steelworks still used as a goal.

A youth on one of the new Chopper bikes nearly ran me over as I turned down the entry.

'Soz, Mrs,' he shouted as he whizzed past.

Did I really look like a Mrs to the younger generation? I entered by the back door where the zinc bath still hung on the outer wall, and went through into the front room. It was strange how we habitually used the back door, even though we spent most time in the front.

'Hello Dad, don't get up,' I said as he rose from his chair. I gave him a waxed bag of Thornton's toffee, a hug and a kiss. 'Where's Mum?'

'Hello, love, she's gone down Hillsborough, meeting Pat, Mary and Doris.'

He had aged since I'd last seen him.

'I'm glad you've come, I could do with a bit of a trim.' He stroked his hand down the back of his head and neck.

I felt in my handbag and took out my scissors.

'Snip, snip.' I waved them in front of him. 'Going to make a cuppa first – do you want one?'

'Aye, go on then, love. By the way, Landlord called round the other day…'

'Oh aye, he's not putting the rent up again, is he?' I interrupted, as he followed me through to the kitchen.

'No, love, the cheeky bugger wanted to know if we wanted to buy the house – at sitting tenant price.'

My ears pricked. Filling the kettle, I put it on the gas ring to boil.

'Did he now? What did you say?'

'I told him to bugger off – that I'd already bought it, ten times over.'

I smiled to myself as I pictured the scene.

'What did Mum have to say?' I took a couple of mugs from the cabinet.

'For once, she agreed with me.'

'What was he asking?'

'Three-hundred quid, the cheeky bugger.'

A thought flashed through my mind and I wondered if John and I could afford to buy it in Mum and Dad's name. Then they wouldn't have to pay any rent, and it would be an investment for us. At least that way we would see something for our money, instead of the measly four and a half per cent in the bank.

'Go and sit back down, Dad, I'll bring it through when it's ready.'

Looking around the kitchen, I saw it was ready for decorating again; at least there was no blackened area above the fireplace since the coal fire had gone. The airing rack was hoisted up to the ceiling: Dad's yellowed long-johns and woolly vests hung over the wooden rails. I went over to the bottom cupboard that my dog Shep had claimed for herself, now back to its original state of housing shoes and boots.

While waiting for the kettle to boil, I looked through the net curtains and up the yard, shared by the four houses, and the block of four toilets with non-fastening doors. Nothing had changed. Sheffield was now supposed to be one of the cleanest cities in Europe.

Only because there's no more industry, the regulars at the Crown jeered, whenever they heard or read that statement. There wasn't much sign of it around here. The same tall, dirty chimneys, the works yard full of rusting ingots and steel bars stacked on broken wooden pallets. Lorries, laden and ready for Monday's early start.

The kettle whistled.

'What do you want, Dad, tea or coffee?'

'I'll have some of that new-fangled coffee your mother's bought. Don't reckon much to it, mind.'

I picked up the bottle and looked at the label: Camp coffee.

'I'll bet she's only bought it because it's got a man wearing a kilt on it.'

Dad chuckled. I poured a teaspoonful of the tarry liquid into a mug and filled it with hot water and milk, then made a pot of tea for me. While the leaves settled, I looked into the pantry with its whitewashed walls, a few tins of fruit, a tin of thick cream, a tin of corned beef and Spam.

On the top shelf was an old biscuit tin, containing buttons and bits of string, sealing wax, nappy pins, broken costume jewellery, curtain hooks and rings. The washing line looped and hung from a hook beneath the bottom shelf with a bag of pegs, bought from gypsies whom Mum feared. The bag was one I had made and embroidered in junior school. The wooden clothes prop stood in the corner.

The stone cellar steps were old and worn, hollowed in the centre, especially the top one, which we used for sharpening knives. Going down the steps where the saucepans were stored upside down along one edge, I remembered the mouse traps I used to set and empty before bed at night and school in the mornings. Luckily, we had very few mice. There were two cellars, one to the front and one to the rear, which we were supposed to use in the event of an air-raid.

I turned into the front cellar. The coal had long gone and the walls were whitewashed. No matter how often Mum swept the cobwebs away, they always managed to re-appear overnight. The row of bricks across the floor for walking on when the rain poured in through the coal grate was still there. They were still used, as the gas meter was situated on the inside of the outer wall. Three shillings were in place on the top, ready for use. The unused mousetraps were on a shelf, along with the hobbing foot which we used for repairing our shoes and putting metal segs into our footwear to make them last longer. Ian always wanted plenty of them in his shoes, as he liked them to spark on the stone flags.

The ceiling laths creaked overhead as I heard Dad walk across the floor. Bits of dust and perished plaster fell with his every step. He was standing in the doorway as I returned and switched off the light.

'Sorry, Dad, I thought I'd have a nosey and see if there's anything you need. Your coffee should be ready to drink now.'

Dad was really my stepfather. He had adopted me when he married Mum. I was four at the time. A year later, my sister had been born and five years afterward, my brother Ian. Dad was the talk of the street: at sixty-five years of age, he had produced a son. Because of the age difference, he couldn't see to Ian's needs like a younger father would.

I looked at him now as he stood. Still quite tall with a slight stoop, his trousers were held up with braces around his shrinking chest and there were wiry grey hairs poking out of the front of his open-necked shirt.

I lit a cigarette; we sat down and talked for a while.

'How's retirement going?' He had turned eighty now, and his age and weak chest had the better of him.

'I don't know. Sometimes I think I was better at work.' He gave a slight laugh. 'It's your mother, always moaning I'm under her feet. If I wash the dishes, I haven't done them right. If I vacuum the carpet, that's not right either, or I've left the eyes in when peeling the potatoes.' He rubbed his gnarled hand over the blood blisters on his head. 'She means well, though I wish she'd pack in some of her jobs.'

'I know what you mean, Dad, she's a lot younger than you and got loads of energy, and she still does too much.' I finished my cigarette and doused it in the sink, took the towel from the hook and placed it round his neck.

'Trouble is, love, with Ian at home and Jo still at college, your mother's money's needed.'

I thought about Ian, now in his teens and all his demands. At least he was getting some money from working part-time in the butchers. Jo would be leaving college soon and taking up a teaching position.

'Yes, you're right, Dad.' I emptied the leaves from the teapot down the sink, poked them around with my finger so they didn't clog the drain and rinsed the mugs. 'Come on, Dad, let's get your hair cut.'

5

Later, I told John about the house.

'I thought we could buy it and they could live rent free.'

'Where would we get three hundred pounds from?' he replied.

'We have some savings, and I have an endowment policy due to pay out twenty-five pounds when I reach twenty-five.'

John sat, deep in thought. 'It's a good idea, and it's an investment.'

'That's what I thought. I know it will set us back a bit, but we'll get over it when we take over the pub.' We both sat, thinking of ways to raise the money.

'I could sell the Spitfire and manage with a cheaper car, so long as it gets us from A to B.'

'No John, I couldn't ask you to do that. You love your fast cars and you no longer ride a motor bike.'

'Perhaps our Harry and Tom would chip in. I'll ask them.'

~

John's brother, who liked a flutter on the horses had just had a big win and offered it to us. We told him we couldn't accept such a large amount; he insisted, saying he would only gamble it away, so we might as well put it to some good use.

Three months later, we managed to get the money together and bought the house in Mum and Dad's name to benefit from the sitting tenant price.

We sold the Spitfire and bought a cheaper car, an Austin Champ which was a British version of the American jeep. It had a pick and a shovel fixed to the side; a five-gallon petrol canister and spare wheel on the back, and an exhaust pipe that rose up into the air, allowing it go in deep water. Although cheap to purchase, the running costs were higher. But it was fun, and instead of having one of the fastest cars on the road, we now had one of the slowest. With six forward and six reverse gears, it could go backwards as fast as forward, which wasn't very fast, as we soon found out. In fact, it could take five minutes to start, the smell of fuel and engine oil filling the air. It had such slow gears, grinding as they groaned and scraped into action, all revs being lost in the process. It also had a hand brake that would occasionally lock itself on.

As it was summer, we took the sides off the vehicle as well as the roof, leaving just the windscreen, which could be folded flat if we were parked: we had tried it down while traveling, and too many flying insects bombarded us.

One Saturday morning, we headed to Scarborough, singing 'Bye Bye Miss American Pie', and 'In the Summertime' with Mungo Jerry. I wore my hair long, with a headband and flowers. My skirt was long and floaty, made of soft cotton and muslin and a cheesecloth top with a drawstring neckline and rows of seed necklaces. Cork-soled espadrilles completed the look. John had grown his hair long and sported a droopy moustache.

Four hours later, we arrived in Scarborough, driving around the streets and waving to similarly-clad people, who whistled and waved back. Then we saw it: the lifeboat ramp. We looked at each other.

'Go, go go!' I shouted, and stood up, holding on the top of the windscreen.

John changed gears, looked around and drove onto the ramp, then down onto the beach, straight into the sea.

'Yahoo!' we screamed as John turned and drove along the beach in two feet of water, the incoming tide splashing up the side. People stopped and stared, others ran alongside and some jumped into the vehicle with us.

'Great stuff, man,' said one guy as he tumbled into the back.

'Born to be wild…' I was singing as loud as I could. The guy in

29

the back joined in as he helped pull others on board. 'Born to be w-i-i -i-l-d.'

We drove as far as the pier, turned around and headed back to the lifeboat ramp. A police car was parked at the top.

'O–oh,' said our passengers, who gradually slid off the jeep. 'Peace, man,' said one and disappeared with the others.

'Party, Peasholm Park, tonight…Join us, plenty of pot,' someone whispered as he took leave.

'No thanks,' I replied. 'Been there, done it. I'll stick with my Park Drive.'

There was just John and I in the jeep when it stopped in front of the police car. Two officers came over. One inspected the vehicle.

'Having fun?' he said, with no amusement in his voice.

The other one checked John's licence and insurance.

'Give us a break, officer,' said John. 'We're on holiday and just arrived.'

The officer took out his notepad and made a note of the registration number and our names and address, then conferred with his partner.

John and I looked at each other in despair; a fine start to the holiday. One of the officers went over to their car, started it up and moved it to one side. The other officer came back and handed John his papers.

'Don't let me see you pull a crazy stunt like that again or any traffic offence, or you'll be for it. You should have more sense at your age. On your way.' He signalled for John to leave and stepped out of the way.

'Thanks, mate, good on yer,' said John and drove onto the main road.

~

After having fun with the Champ during the summer, we found it none too comfortable for the winter months, although it could get around whatever the weather. But without insulation, it was too cold.

With the help of Hire Purchase, we bought a newer model Triumph Spitfire. John continued working at Tinsley Wire, and was given the position of foreman joiner, which he took willingly when his old boss retired. I continued full-time at the Crown, to which we were no nearer taking over.

My brother left school at sixteen and was offered a job at a large wholesale butcher's. He would be paid full rate, owing to his previous experience and would be in the position of manager when he reached eighteen.

However, Ian decided he wanted to work down the road at Owlerton Dog Track as a dog handler. Mum and Dad were livid: he had learnt a trade that would secure his future working life and earn him good money at a young age. There was no changing him: he had made his decision, and being spoilt, had his way.

My sister, Jo, never came back home. She qualified as a teacher and found a teaching position in North Yorkshire, near where she had trained.

6

Months turned into years and life was good, apart from the mounting tension with the government and the miners. As such, it didn't affect us, living in the city away from the mining areas, apart from experiencing power-cuts for hours at a time, morning, afternoon or evening.

Living in the tower blocks gave us another problem, not so much for the younger able-bodied generation, to us it was more of an inconvenience, yet to the older people who lived on each floor in the one-bedroom flats, it was a nightmare, with lifts out of action and only emergency lighting. Some lit candles, which were accidentally knocked over, causing even more problems for the firemen and ambulance men.

Most of the tenants, being good natured, generally took it in their stride to keep an eye on their elderly neighbours, especially the ones on the high levels. As for the surrounding areas, Derbyshire, Rotherham, Doncaster and Barnsley, they were in the midst of the unrest, and disputes grumbled on like a rumbling volcano.

~

A new type of holiday was all the rage and travel agents were springing up everywhere. Cheap package holidays to Spain became available to the working classes. Flights and accommodation could be booked in one operation; two weeks on the Costa Brava or Costa Dorada would cost as little as twenty-nine pounds per person.

It was morning in mid-January and we were finishing a breakfast of cornflakes and milk. It was our turn for the morning power cuts, so no cooked breakfast. The under floor heating wasn't on, nor was the two-bar electric fire. With the flats being all-electric, owing to the Ronan Point disaster in London a few years ago, gas supplies were now banned in high-rise flats.

The large steel-framed, single-glazed windows offered little protection from the cold winds that blew around the top of the block. At one hundred and fifty feet above the ground, on one of Sheffield's highest hills, it was no place for the frail, and vertigo sufferers, as Dad found out when he first visited the flat. It wasn't long before we had to take him home, as it made him feel too ill.

John was reading the morning paper.

'How about this, Jack? A week in Tenerife for only thirty-nine pounds, flying from Manchester?' He lowered the paper so I could see.

'I'm not sure, John – you know I don't like the idea of flying.' I placed my spoon in the dish and looked over at John's bowl. 'Have you finished?' I asked.

'Yes, thanks. Didn't like that, not like a hearty breakfast.'

I collected the bowls and took them into the kitchen, leaving the pots on the side; no hot water to wash them. Snow had covered the balcony and the view over the park and city was spectacular, despite being so grey and cold.

'What do you think?' John called.

It was tempting. He took hold of my hand.

'Come on, Jack. It'll do you good. Your chest has been terrible lately.' His blue eyes pleaded.

'But John, you know how fussy you are with food. You don't know what you're going to get abroad. Besides, neither of us have got a passport.'

'I can soon get one, and I think I can include you in mine. I'll call in the post office and collect a form.'

I could see the disappointment in his eyes.

'Okay then, let's go.' I kissed the top of his head. 'I'll go and tell Mum and Dad this afternoon, when you've gone to the match.'

~

'Hiya Dad,' I said, giving him a hug. 'Mum not in?'

'She's meeting Pat and Doris in the Shakespeare,' said Dad, sitting back in the chair and lighting his pipe.

'Mum going in a pub? That's a laugh.' I lit a cigarette and sat down opposite Dad.

'She went last week as well – looks like it might become a regular occurrence.' He puffed away on his pipe until it caught alight.

I looked at my fingernails, chewed almost to the wick. My little finger had a whitlow which I kept picking, making it worse.

'Have you heard from Jo?' I asked.

'Aye, I think a letter came during the week, have a look at the back of the clock.'

I took a few quick drags on the cigarette and reached behind the clock. There was a Littlewoods football coupon, a collection envelope from the Salvation Army and an electric bill, which Dad insisted he wasn't going to pay because of the cuts. He didn't quite grasp that he would still only be paying for what he had used.

'No, nothing there,' I said, and put everything back as I had found it.

'She's perhaps took it with her to show Pat and Doris.'

'Yes, she'll be bragging about how well Jo's doing.' I took another drag on the cigarette and stubbed it out in Dad's ashtray.

A shadow passed by the window and Dad stood up. 'Talk of the devil, she's here now.'

Mum entered, unsteady on her feet, her face flushed. I gave her a hug and kissed her cheek. She smelled of alcohol.

'Have you been drinking, Mum?' She was swaying.

'I've only had a couple with our Pat, Doris and Mary. We've started meeting up in the Shakespeare every Saturday.' She put the kettle on the stove.

'I didn't think you drank alcohol. Dad could never get you to have a drink, even at Christmas.'

'I drank when I was carrying Jo. Your dad said to have some Guinness, as it made bonny babies. And it did – Jo weighed in at a similar birth weight to you and Ian put together.'

She poured a spoonful of tar into a mug and added the boiling water, spilling some over the side.

'What do you drink now then, apart from Camp coffee – Guinness?' I asked.

'Yes, I've took a liking to Gold Labels. Our Pat drinks them.' She sipped the scalding hot black liquid.

'Mum,' I snapped. 'Gold Labels are too strong for you. You shouldn't be drinking alcohol at all if you're taking blood pressure pills.'

'I don't tell you what to drink, so don't you tell me.' She looked at me with glazed eyes. 'I'll say goodbye now. I'm going in the front room to watch the wrestling – Mick McManus and Jackie Pallo are on.' She carried the mug of coffee with her. There were no goodbye hugs or kisses.

'Well,' said Dad. 'That's told you.'

7

Dave nudged me. I came back to the present.

'Drinks from the bar,' the hostess said.

'Sorry,' I replied, sitting up and realising my seat belt was still fastened. 'I was miles away.'

'We all are up here,' she smiled.

'I'll have a Rémy Martin and lemonade, please.' I pulled the seat table down in front of me.

Dave shuffled, uncomfortable in his position and ordered a Bacardi and Coke. He was too big for airline seating.

The hostess placed the drinks on the table along with a couple of paper coasters and two small packets of nuts. Dave paid and she moved the trolley forward.

We were about an hour into the flight, two more to go. We must have been thinking along the same lines as we looked at each other and smiled weakly. I took a drink from the plastic glass, hoping it would settle my churning stomach.

Dave's arm brushed mine as he raised the glass to his lips. I wanted him to pull me into his arms and hold me forever. Taking hold of his hand, my stomach calmed and my heart skipped a beat as I thought back to when we'd first met, two years ago.

~

John and I had been in our flat for over eight years. I had left the wholesale chemist's and was still in touch with the friends I had made. I still went out with them on Fridays.

Coming back from the Crown one afternoon, I entered the block via the ground floor and pressed the lift call button. It was empty when it arrived. I stepped inside.

'Hold the lift!' I heard someone shout. I pressed the door open button.

'Thanks, love,' a middle aged woman said as she entered and placed her shopping bags on the floor.

'What floor are you going to?' I asked.

'Eight,' she replied.

I pressed the eight button and then the fourteen. The doors closed and the lift went down to the basement. The doors opened and two workmen entered. They were tall and heavyset. Rugby players sprang to mind. The lift floor adjusted slightly as it accommodated their weight. I moved further back. The woman moved her bags as the lift began its ascent. One of the workers held a large tool bag, the other a batch of work sheets.

'The's not much room in here wi' you two big buggers,' the woman said, laughing.

'It's not every day you get as lucky as this, love, is it?' one of them replied. 'Two handsome fellers escorting you.' They looked down at her and laughed.

'If I were a few years younger, I'd have you escort me anytime,' she said, then looked at me and winked. She winked again and nodded her head in their direction.

I gave them a small smile in acknowledgement and looked away. They smiled back, their stares a fraction too long. One of them raised an eyebrow and glanced at the other, who pursed his lips slightly. They stretched themselves up to full height and changed their stance. There was barely an inch between the metal ceiling of the lift and the tops of their heads. The lift stopped.

'Not coming to my flat then?' said the woman as she picked up her bags and stepped out.

'If your name's on this list, love, we'll be seeing you,' said the man holding the worksheets.

She laughed and went on her way. The lift doors began to close, when a woman pushing a pram rushed along the corridor.

'Just a minute!' she shouted.

The men held back the doors.

'Thanks,' she said and pushed the pram inside the lift. 'Oh, sorry, are you going up?' she added, as the lift moved. 'Never mind, I'll have a longer ride.'

To make room for the pram, the two men had to step back. They were now well into my space. I could smell putty and flux. Instead of facing the front, they were leaning on the lift walls facing each other, glancing towards me and grinning slightly.

I was well aware of the meaning behind their actions; I was used to being in the company of more men than these two and wouldn't let myself be intimidated by them. I glanced up at their side profiles; they were handsome. The dark-haired man was probably fractionally taller than the fair-haired one.

'Top deck,' he said, as the lift stopped.

The woman with the pram had to step back out, allowing them to pass. I followed and expected them to turn left or right before they reached the stairwell. When they realised I was behind them, they stepped aside.

'After you,' said one.

'Looks like we're going all the way together,' said his partner, a cheeky grin on his face.

Smiling, the other bowed and swept his arm in front of him.

I was wearing a cropped skinny-rib jumper, a very short miniskirt, white leather knee-high platform boots and a chambray denim Carnaby Street cap. I didn't want to go in front of them. I raised my hand and moved it to the left.

'No, you were out first, go ahead,' I said and motioned for them to go up the steps.

They stood, one at either side of the staircase, looking up and waiting. One of them began to whistle; the other joined in.

I nodded my head upwards.

'Go on,' I urged. They didn't move. Neither did I. It was a stalemate. I tried to fix my gaze and stay put, but their grins were catching. I closed my eyes, sighed and began to laugh. They'd won. I walked past them and up the steps, holding the handrail, my eyes closed as they followed.

On reaching the top, I stopped, expecting them to turn right; they didn't. They were still behind me on the steps.

I took a step forward and turned left; they did too. Pulling open the fire door, I entered the lobby and carried on walking to the second fire door. I stopped again, the footsteps behind me stopped.

'Look, what's going on?' I said, turning on them.

They made a big show of jumping back and cowering. Grinning, I pulled the door open, walked to my flat door, took the keys from my handbag and placed one in the lock. I heard keys jangle and turned my head. One of the men held a set of keys similar to mine.

'Tell me – what's going on?' I asked, unlocking the door.

'Mind your own business, and get that kettle on,' said the dark-haired one. 'We're not asking you what you're doing.' He opened the door next to mine. 'Come on, Dave, let's get this bathroom fixed. Can't stand out here gossiping to the housewives all day.'

My mouth opened. Of all the cheek.

The second man popped his head back around the door.

'Two teas, milk and sugar, love,' he said and winked.

Laughing to myself, I put the kettle on to boil. I had never seen much of my old neighbours, as they had been out at work all day and I had never been inside their flat. Our flat faced South West; next door faced North West and while the flat was empty, I wanted to take this opportunity to see the different views.

The door was open.

'Where shall I put these?' I asked, looking around. There was no furniture on which to place the mugs.

The dark-haired chap who was working on the washbasin, turned.

'Put them on the kitchen worktop, we'll get them in a minute. What's your name?' He pulled the washbasin from the wall and placed it on the floor.

'Jackie,' I replied.

'Nice name,' said the fair-haired chap, lying on his back and disconnecting the bath. His chest and arms were huge and the muscles and veins along his neck stood proud as he turned the wrench to free the connection.

I looked around the empty flat, comparing the fixtures, which were identical, and the views from the windows couldn't compare. The windows overlooked the cemetery and crematorium. Thick black smoke swirled up into the sky. I looked away.

'Not as good a view as yours, eh?' shouted one of them.

'No, nothing like,' I made my way back to the bathroom. 'Why are you removing the fittings?'

'They need replacing before the next tenants move in. Never let it be said that the council doesn't look after its tenants.'

'Do you always replace the fittings when new people are coming in?' I asked.

'No, only if they're damaged. The washbasin is cracked and the bath is chipped.'

'My washbasin's cracked,' I replied.

They glanced at each other. 'Better take a look at that, Dave.' The dark haired one nodded.

Within minutes, all the bathroom fittings were free.

They stood up and stretched their limbs. 'Right, let's get that tea.'

'What's your names?' I asked, as the three of us made our way into the kitchen.

'I'm Dave and this is Dave,' the dark-haired one said as he pointed to his right.

I looked up at them. 'You're kidding.'

'You can call me Dave and him Little Dave, seeing as he's half an inch shorter than me.' He laughed and gave a friendly punch to his partner's arm.

'I can't call anyone over six foot little.'

'Dave'll do. Anyhow, where's the cake?' said Little Dave as he picked up the mug of tea.

'What cake? You didn't say anything about cake, you only asked for tea.'

'I'd have thought a good-looking girl like you would know that cake is served with afternoon tea,' said Big Dave, grinning.

'Oh! Hold on a minute, I'll go and bake one.' I turned as if to walk out of the kitchen.

They drank their tea. 'Thanks, sorry can't wash them, no water,' said Dave, as he handed me the mugs. 'Come on, let's look at this washbasin of yours.'

'I'll just nip down to the van, I need to check something,' said Big Dave.

Little Dave followed me. His arm brushed mine, causing the fine hairs to stand on end as we went inside.

'Static,' I said, as I rubbed my arm.

He looked me in the eyes. 'Or something,' he replied, and rubbed his arm.

He'd felt it too. I looked away. There was an awkward silence. He made his way down the hall.

'This is some pad you've got here, Jackie,' he said and looked around. 'Do you mind?'

'No, not at all, feel free,' I said, quite pleased and proud of my choice of furnishings and décor. I followed him into the lounge.

He looked amazed. 'Who did all this?' His eyes scoured the room.

'Me.' I put a finger to my mouth and quickly removed it, keeping my fingernails out of sight.

'Well, you're not just a pretty face, are you?'

I looked away. What was the matter with me? I was used to flattery. It was commonplace, working in the pub. I wasn't in the pub now; I was alone with a strange man in the privacy of my home.

He moved towards the fireplace. 'Have you painted these?' he said, looking at the abstract paintings.

'Yes, I did those years ago and then when I decorated the flat, I thought the pictures would look perfect in this room. My husband made the frames, and I painted them white to make the colours stand out. I would normally have used black paint, but these needed lifting.'

'What a gal.' He whistled and made his way back towards the kitchen. 'Can't do much with the kitchen, everything's already fitted,' he said, glancing into the room.

'So well designed though. Every inch of space has been well thought out.'

He walked towards the large bedroom and placed his hand on the door handle. I remained in the kitchen.

'May I?' he asked, turning his head towards me.

I nodded and looked away and wondered what he would think to the fitted, ivory painted wardrobes, full-length dressing unit and mirror John had installed, with subdued lighting behind the king-size bed.

Big Dave came back just at the right time. 'Can I come in?' he asked as he knocked and came down the hallway. He was laughing.

'I've just seen Bas.' He looked at Dave, who glanced my way as he came from the bedroom.

Big Dave couldn't speak for laughing. He tried again, and folded over. After a minute, he continued.

'Oh God!' He tried to compose himself. 'Bas says that new lad we sent to the depot for a long stand just before lunch…' He broke off again, still laughing and managing to catch his breath. 'He's still there…'

His laughter was catching. Dave burst out laughing and so did I, even though I didn't know what at. We were all in the hallway.

Eventually, the laughter ceased.

'Let's have a look at this crack,' said Dave, as the two of them, still chuckling, moved into the bathroom.

Dave examined it. 'How'd it happen?'

'My husband, he dropped the drill on it when he was fitting the cabinet.'

'Ah! Wilful damage to council property – that's a punishable offence.'

My jaw dropped as I looked at Big Dave. 'What?'

'Take no notice of him, he's having you on. Still thinks he's in the police force,' said Dave, laughing. 'I'll put you down for a replacement.'

'What, a replacement husband?' I joked as he made notes in his book. They grinned.

'It'll be some time next week. Any particular day?'

'No,' I replied. 'I leave at ten-thirty and I'm back after three-thirty.'

They made their way back to the other flat and picked up their tools. Dave placed the key in the lock.

'We'll be back to finish this job at eight in the morning. Bacon sarnies will go down well.' He winked and locked the door behind him.

'No sauce on mine though,' said Big Dave. 'See you tomorrow.'

Cheeky devils I thought, as I went back into the flat. I looked over the balcony as they climbed into their grey PWD van. Dave looked up. I stepped back. I realised I'd better get the tea on; John would be home soon.

~

The plane began its descent into Manchester Ringway airport. Air Hostesses stowed their trolleys, collected empty glasses and bottles, checked seatbelts and handed out barley sugar sweets.

Dave and I sat in silence, holding hands. We had come to the end of our journey. The plane dipped its right wing, turned and moved into a deeper descent. My heart did too.

The hydraulics released the landing gear, which clunked, locking the wheels in position. We could now see the lights of Manchester below, in between the speeding clouds. Then we were in thick cloud again. Rain splattered the windows.

'Cabin crew seated for landing.' The captain's voice came over the speaker system.

I leaned as far as I could over Dave, as the lights of the runway came up towards us. With a heavy clunk, we landed, the nose lowered and the front wheels touched down a second later. The engines roared with reverse thrust as the plane continued, its power fading as it slowed and then taxied off the runway to its parking bay.

We waited until all the other travellers had left the plane and then made our way down the steps in the pouring rain. Sidestepping other passengers, we ran across the tarmac into the airport building.

Joining the queue at passport control, we were face-checked and waved through to the baggage claim area. We stood and looked at each other, too choked to speak. Our cases arrived and we made our way towards customs and the arrivals hall, where John would be waiting. Before going through, Dave stopped, put the cases down and pulled me into his arms.

'Dave, no, please.' People were staring. We kissed for what seemed an eternity. I clung to him; he then pulled away, yet held onto my arms, his eyes bright with anger, frustration and passion. He looked up to the ceiling and then at me.

'I'll never give you up, never.'

He picked up the cases and we exited into the real world.

John was waiting in Arrivals, his face grim. I gave him a hug and told him I had missed him.

'Missed you too,' he said and led us to the Jag, parked outside the large glass doors. He unlocked it.

Dave placed the cases in the boot and got into the back of the car. I sat in the front with John. No one spoke.

John started the engine; it purred into life, and then growled as only an XK150 can. It pulled away from the airport, towards Stockport.

The rain was still pouring as he drove away from the fuel-heavy skies. I watched the wipers rhythmically sweeping left to right, left to right, and was lulled into a false state of security. As warm and silent as it was in the car, the tension was strained. This was how John handled any issues: he wouldn't talk about them, remaining silent was his manner.

I recalled the night he told me that he knew about my affair with Dave. He had been exceptionally quiet and I knew something was amiss.

~

'What do you intend doing about it?' he said, nothing more. His face told me he'd found out.

'About what?' I said, stupidly, and looked away, my guilt already showing.

'Don't take me for a fool, Jack, you know what.'

I didn't know what to say. *Don't be ridiculous, you're imagining things, or, what gives you that idea?* He waited for an answer.

'Let me make it easy for you. Is it going to continue?' His blue eyes burned into mine; he stood still.

I began to fidget and didn't know where to look.

'John, I'm sorry.' I began to cry.

'So am I,' he replied, ignoring my tears, whereas at one time he would have taken me in his arms and kissed my tears away whatever the reason. This time, I cried alone.

'Are you planning on leaving?' He turned, went over to the window and looked out.

I jumped at the sudden movement.

'No…I mean, yes…no – I don't know what I mean.' Tears streamed down my face. I went over to him. 'John, I'm so very sorry. It was only supposed to be a bit of fun.'

I took hold of his hand. He pulled away, then turned towards me.

'A bit of fun! At my expense, huh? Am I no longer fun? Are you bored, is that it?'

I slumped in the chair, feeling wretched.

'I don't know what more you want.' He raised his voice. 'Don't we have a good living, nice cars, holidays, clothes, parties? You go out with your girlfriends and flirt with the men. Isn't that enough?'

'I don't know,' I sobbed. 'I just don't know.'

And I didn't. I loved John more than anything or anyone else in the world.

'Well you'd better know by tomorrow.' He closed the door behind him as he went to bed, leaving me alone with my misery.

I lay on the settee, crying until the small hours, and must have dozed. I awoke feeling cold and sick. I crept to bed and cuddled up to John. He wasn't asleep and he ignored me.

~

At eight a.m., I awoke, feeling terrible. My stomach churned and my chest and throat burned. The bed was empty. Getting up, I went to the bathroom and looked in the mirror. My eyes would barely open. I hadn't looked this bad since Shep died. I began to cry again. I didn't know what to do.

I hated myself. I loved John so much, how could I have hurt him so? Even last night, he was gentle with me. A lesser man would have thrown me out; and my lovely clothes too. He loved me more than life itself. I turned my face into the pillow and sobbed, hoping I would suffocate.

There was a gentle knock on the door. It was Dave. I turned over, ignoring him. He knocked again. I pulled John's pillow over my head and lay still. Unable to breathe, I threw the pillow off and turned onto my back. I cast my mind back to the spring of that significant year, when they had returned the following day to finish the job.

8

'Are those bacon sarnies ready yet?' shouted Big Dave as he knocked on my door.

'No they're not,' I replied, opening the door. 'The tea's just mashed; I'll bring it round in a minute.'

I had dressed in low-waist pale denim hot pants, with sheer ten denier tan tights, teamed with a fine-knit, white cropped sweater and my fabulous white patent knee-high boots. I had semi-straightened my long, dark hair.

'Tea's ready,' I called, as I entered the flat next door.

'Wow! That's a sight for sore eyes, Dave,' said Big Dave as he turned.

'Not half,' the other Dave said, his green-brown eyes glistening.

Suddenly remembering, Big Dave raised his nose in the air. 'Can't smell the bacon.'

'Can't have everything,' I replied cockily, leaning against the bathroom wall.

'It's to be hoped you get better looked after next week, Dave.' Big Dave winked as he looked over to his workmate.

'Do you live round here?' I asked casually.

'No, do you?'

'Aha! Very funny,' I replied. They went on to tell me where they lived and we discussed the different areas of Sheffield.

'Are you married?' I asked.

'Divorced,' answered Dave.

Big Dave choked on his tea and looked across at his pal.

'Well, that's a new one on me. Since when?' They both laughed.

We chatted some more and I looked at my watch.

'Well, work calls, I have to leave now,' I said. 'Will you still be here this afternoon?'

'No, we'll have finished by lunch-time,' Big Dave replied.

'Okay, see you around, have a good weekend.' I looked at Dave as I turned to leave.

'I'll see you on Monday, eight o'clock.' He stood up, tall and straight, and wiped his hands on a cloth. His eyes held mine.

I looked away. 'Aren't you coming too?' I said to Big Dave.

'Naa, he doesn't need me to hold his hand on this one,' he said.

They looked at each other and grinned.

'See you Monday then,' I said, looking at Dave. My stomach flipped as he acknowledged me.

That same evening, I went around town with the girls, yet my thoughts were elsewhere. We finished in Tiffany's as usual. The dance floor was crowded. Girls danced around their handbags, trying to entice the opposite sex, or whatever! Blokes stood around watching, holding pints of their favourite beer. We joined the queue, six deep at the bar.

I looked around while we waited. He couldn't possibly be here. Maybe, if he was divorced – or was he? Stop it, I told myself, but knew it was impossible.

After getting served, we sang along with Marvin Gaye, nodding our heads and singing to each other…'I heard it through the Grapevine'. We stood and talked for a while, and then walked around the floor, looking for attractive males, moving on to the dance floor near likely ones. My eyes were scanning for the fair-haired ones, over six foot; one in particular. We danced and flirted as the night wore on, and I was still looking for the one. What if I did see him, and he was with a woman? He could be. He could be with his wife. Did he have a wife? I dismissed the idea. Men don't take their wives and girlfriends to nightclubs, for the same reasons that women don't take their husbands and boyfriends.

48

The night was ending and instead of smooching with someone to the sounds of Percy Sledge and 'When a Man Loves a Woman', I made my way to the cloakroom. I met up with the others in the foyer and lit a cigarette.

'You're quiet tonight, Jackie. Is it that time of the month?' Jacqui, my namesake asked.

'No, just got other things on my mind.' I took a deep drag on the cigarette. 'Didn't see anyone I fancied.'

'Never mind, better luck next week,' she said, and we went outside. I took a last drag on my cigarette, dropped it on the steps and trod on it.

'See you next week,' I said.

~

John was home before me and was fast asleep in bed. I hardly slept that night.

Tossing and turning; my thoughts were always returning to the handsome plumber. I couldn't help myself, and kept thinking what it would be like to be in his arms, and more. I also wondered if he felt the same. There was certainly something there, like an electric current – felt, yet not seen.

The weekend dragged by and as soon as John left for work on Monday morning, I showered, dressed and made extra effort with my make-up and hair. At ten past eight, a quiet knock came on the door. My stomach flipped.

'Hello,' I said, as I opened it.

He stood, completely at ease, his left forearm resting against the top of the doorframe, biceps bulging, tool bag by his side on the floor.

'Morning,' he replied, looking down at me. He didn't move.

'Come in,' I said, stepping aside, avoiding eye contact.

He lifted the tool bag, his brawny frame filling the doorway as he entered and rubbed his boots on the mat. He bent over.

'There's no need to remove them,' I said. 'By the time you've got to the fifteenth floor, any dirt will have gone.'

He smiled, and looked at me the way he had on Friday.

I watched as he walked towards the bathroom, self-assured, confident. His back was broad, covered with a size-too-small white t-shirt; Brutus jeans, tight on muscular thighs.

He interrupted my fantasy.

'First things first,' he said, as he found the stopcock. 'Is there any water in the kettle before I turn it off?'

'Yes, it's recently boiled. I knew it wouldn't be long before you'd want tea. Are you ready now?'

'Yes please, and is that bacon I can smell cooking?' he said, taking a spanner from his bag.

I sniffed. 'Bacon?'

'Wishful thinking,' he replied. 'I'll have to wait till lunch time, and get one of Betty's Big Baps.'

'Betty's Big Baps, what's that?'

'She's got a kiosk at the bottom of the estate, near the depot, does a roaring trade,' he said, as he disconnected the cracked washbasin.

'I'll bet she does, with a name like that,' I replied, looking down at my small breasts.

'Do you want me to make you one?' I asked, sweetly.

'Well, now you're talking. Thought you'd never ask.' He grinned.

I went into the kitchen and opened the fridge.

'Two eggs, please,' he shouted from the bathroom.

I gave him the bacon and egg sandwich and mug of tea and returned to the kitchen to prepare dinner. John loved his dinner as soon as he came home from work, which was no problem for me while not working full time. But today was delivery day at the pub and I wouldn't finish until four.

I peeled the potatoes and carrots, trimmed and washed the cauliflower, then cut the fat off the pork chops and put everything back in the fridge. After finishing the rest of my chores, I went back to the bathroom.

'How long will you be?'

'Six foot two, why?'

I loved his sense of humour; it only added to his attractions.

'I've got to leave at half past ten,' I replied.

'I'll be done by then. Just got to fetch the washbasin from the van and fit it. I'll give you a lift if you want. Mind you, it's only the works van, not like your sports car.'

'How do you know we've got a sports car?'

'I've seen your husband come home in it. White Triumph Spitfire.'

'How do you know…?'

'Not be a minute. Just going for the washbasin.' He winked and grinned at the surprised look on my face.

He fitted the washbasin, the muscles flexing in his arms.

'How'd you get such big muscles?' I asked.

'What muscles? I'll bet you've got bigger muscles pulling all those pints.'

I looked down at my skinny arms and the tiny muscle in my upper right.

'This one, you mean?' I said, and laughed.

'That's a muscle? I've see bigger knots in cotton thread.' His eyes sparkled and crinkled at the edges.

I laughed. 'Aren't you ever serious?'

'Only with friends and people I don't know,' he replied.

'Come on, be serious for once.' A silly grin covered my face.

'Okay. Boxing.'

Boxing? That would explain his air of total confidence.

'How come you haven't got a broken nose?'

'I'm too good,' he laughed.

'Modest, as well.' I wasn't letting up. 'Have you really done boxing?'

'Nah, the muscles come from carrying the cast iron baths into the Park Hill flats when I was an apprentice.' He wiped around the sink with a cloth. 'Don't look so disappointed. I boxed at school and can give as good as I get – if not more, if need be.'

'You must have been good. Were you?'

'The teacher thought so, but Mum and Dad wouldn't hear of it.'

I looked at my watch. It was almost time to go. Dave reconnected the water supply while I collected my things from the bedroom.

'Are you ready?' he asked, as he put his tools back in the bag. 'Don't want to leave anything. Might have to come back.' He laughed.

I handed him a sandwich and a Kit Kat as we made our way to the door.

'Lunch,' I said, as we stepped into the outer hall. *Can't have you going to Betty's Big Baps, you might get ideas.*

'Thanks,' he replied and began to unwrap the greaseproof paper. 'What is it?'

'Roast beef. I hope that's okay?' I locked the door as we stepped into the outer hall and walked towards the fire door.

With his tool bag over his arm, he peeled the wrapper from the Kit Kat and stuffed the wrapper in his pocket, opened the sandwich and placed the Kit Kat on top of the meat between the two slices of bread.

'What on earth are you doing?'

'Gaffer's in today, so it'll have to be a quickie.' He grinned, pulled the door open and took a bite of the sandwich and Kit Kat while he waited for me to pass.

'It's only half-past ten,' I said.

He winked as he took another bite. By the time the lift reached the basement, the sandwich had gone.

He drove me to the bus station where I could catch the bus to the Crown.

'Thanks,' I said, as I jumped out of the van. 'See you around,' I added, hopefully.

'Hope so,' he replied. 'Thanks for the sandwiches, much better than Betty's.' He reached over and checked the door; looked in his rear view and side mirror. The indicators flashed.

'Call in anytime you're in the block,' I called. *Oh God! What on earth made me say that?*

'Will do.' He winked again, and gave a blast on the horn as he pulled away.

A thrill ran through my body and a grin spread over my face. Trying hard not to look like a love-struck teenager, I made my way to the end of the bus queue.

~

He did call in. So what? It was only a bit of fun, and I enjoyed his company. He was two years younger than me; he was separating from his wife and had two children.

We talked about work and swapped jokes, neither of us overstepping the mark. Each visit became more intense. I began to realise I was venturing down a wayward path. I lost sleep lying awake, re-living the little time we spent together.

9

I was having problems with my throat and tonsils as well as my ailing chest. I had cut down on cigarettes and was now smoking ten a day.

I was also due at the Family Planning Association, which I was dreading. A new doctor's practice had opened nearby and I decided to try it. The doctor was a lot younger than the older ones at the other surgery; he also offered family planning services. The first time I saw him, I was shocked. His arm was in a sling and he sported a black eye.

'Well, you're a fine advert for your profession,' I said.

He laughed. 'Saturday's rugby match. We won though – take a seat.'

'I should hate to see the losing side,' I replied and sat down.

He looked to be a similar age to me and I felt comfortable with him. I told him about my issues with the clinic and that they were reluctant to supply me with the pill as I had been on it continuously since I was twenty-one, and now I was almost thirty, I should have started having children.

'Don't you want children?'

'Yes…and no? When we were first married, we wanted kids a lot. Things changed – I realised there was so much more you could do without them, and as we would be taking over the pub where we worked, I didn't think it was the right place for children.'

'What does your husband think?'

'We've talked about it. He's not bothered either way. He says the decision's mine. So we decided to leave it until nearer my thirties and then decide, and now I'm almost there, we're in a sort of comfort zone, and perfectly happy as we are. Aunt Doris says we should be thinking about who's going to look after us when we're old. I don't think that's the right reason to have children. Besides, what if they emigrate? Then what?'

'You obviously know what you want. Have you thought of alternative contraception?'

'We used condoms until the pill became available, and my mum used a cap.' I smiled to myself as I remembered my early teens and thought it was something to wear on the head. 'I've heard women talk of the coil…'

'Wouldn't recommend it for you, my dear,' he interrupted. 'I would only recommend it for women who have had children by natural section.' He made a few notes. 'So, the Pill it is then. What are you taking now?'

'Gynovlar 21,' I replied.

'Providing you have regular check-ups and cervical smears, there is no reason for you not to continue with it.'

'I am. I don't have any problems with taking it.'

'Of course, you must remember that many drugs carry certain risks if taken over a long period, and that's the risk you must be prepared to take. As doctors, we can only give you the facts and offer advice. I have a Family Planning clinic every alternate Thursday. Have a word with Cynthia on your way out and she will make you an appointment. Now, is there anything else I can help you with?'

I told him of my recurring chest, throat problems and septic tonsils. He examined my throat and listened to my chest.

'Tonsils give you many problems?' he asked.

'Yes, clears up and then comes back.'

'Might be as well to have them taken out.'

He reached for a form off the shelf and began filling it in. 'You're going to have stop smoking, otherwise you are heading for serious health issues.'

'I have cut down and smoke filter-tipped now. I've never tried to stop before.'

'Well now's the time, the tonsillectomy is a serious operation.'

'What? When my brother had his removed, he was out of hospital the same day and eating ice cream.'

'I suppose he was about eight years old at the time?' He peered at me with one lovely clear brown eye; the other was dark and full of blood with a blue and purple surround.

'Yes, he was,' I replied.

He laughed, and then grimaced.

'Sore ribs,' he said, suppressing a grin. 'You will need to book two weeks off work, as you will be in hospital for one of them…'

'A week? Why so long?'

'An adult's tonsils are far larger than a child's. The waiting list, by the way, is a year. I will try for priority placing, and cannot promise anything. Meanwhile, I will prescribe you a low-dose penicillin tablet, one daily, which I will issue on repeat prescription.'

I left the new doctor's feeling pleased. The new doctor was a lovely man whom I felt comfortable with, and I was glad that I didn't have to go back to the FPA clinic at Eversure House.

~

A few days later, John's passport arrived and I was looking forward to the holiday, if not the flight, and the thought of not seeing Dave for a week.

I began packing days in advance, unsure what to take for a foreign holiday, and then decided to stick with summer clothes.

We drove over the moors in the early morning and parked in the long-stay car park. I found the noise and smell of the airport at Ringway, Manchester frightening and yet thrilling at the same time.

Long chandeliers hung in the departure lounge; a bar was open during non-licensed hours, selling alcoholic drinks and snacks. I was full of excitement and expectation at the experience of Passport Control; John showing his passport. His picture and mine were given close scrutiny and then the black booklet was stamped accordingly and handed back. We stepped over the marked line; we were no longer in England, yet were we still in Britain?

We were travelling in a Comet 4B, a plane with a central aisle and two seats aligned on either side. Our first stop was at Gatwick, to pick up other passengers and then on to Madeira, where we had to refuel because of head winds.

The experience of take-off, where we were thrown back in our seats, flying up through dark clouds into brilliant sunshine, banking left and right, where I leaned the opposite way, and the rest of the flight, although strange, was uneventful, much to my relief.

Passengers read books, magazines and newspapers, plus the flight sheet, passed around the cabin from the on-board navigator. It didn't make any sense to me. I was only too aware of how far we were from the ground and all the more so over the Atlantic Ocean.

It was dark when we arrived at Los Rodeos airport in the north of Tenerife, seven hours later. The coach seemed to take forever as it journeyed to the south of the island and to the resort of El Médano. Strange and different scents wafted through the open windows with extreme warmth. Our clothes were sticking to our bodies when we arrived at the hotel. How could it be so hot?

Although tired from the long day, the strangeness of a different land and people kept us awake and we were in no hurry to go to bed. We were shown to our room, which was clean and basic with crisp cotton sheets on the beds.

'Twin beds. I didn't expect that, did you?'

'Probably because of the heat,' John replied.

A glass door opened onto a balcony. We stepped outside. All kinds of sounds could be heard, some like large crickets, others I'd never heard before.

'What on earth are they?' I looked at John. He looked as bewildered as me. We didn't have a sea view; the room overlooked a garden which was dimly lit and full of flowers and shrubs, different from the ones we had at home. Their scents mingled with the night heat.

I went into the bathroom.

'John, come and look at this,' I said. We had our own shower, a wash basin on a pedestal, and a toilet. Another ceramic fitting was placed beside the toilet, which looked like another lavatory, without a lid.

'What do you think that's for?'

'Must be to wash your feet,' said John, a puzzled look on his face.

'Oh John, isn't it nice to have our own shower and toilet.'

The following morning, breakfast was served in a large dining room and consisted of small bread rolls, tiny foil-covered pieces of butter and individual pots of jams and marmalade. Boiled eggs could be had on request. There was coffee, and tea made from tea bags. There was no bacon or sausages, fried eggs or fried bread: apparently these were classed as dinner items.

We walked to the sandy beach and lay in the sunshine, marvelling at the wonders of another country. When it became too warm, we paddled and sat at the edge of the sea, as neither of us could swim. Afterwards, we ventured down the narrow streets and looked at the souvenirs and gift shops.

The Spanish restaurants looked tempting, but we were too afraid to try them. The older Spaniards were dressed in Moorish robes and Gypsies were selling lace tablecloths for a few pesetas.

I had to buy one for Mum. We ate in the hotel restaurant that night. Unsure about what we were ordering, we told the waiter we wanted chicken and chips, which duly arrived, sitting on a plate of greasy liquid. As we were hungry, we ate it, unsure whether it was actually chicken as each leg was bigger than most dogs' legs.

Within two days, we were very much in need of our own toilet, as we both had food poisoning and were suffering with terrible sickness and diarrhoea. I managed to get the room-maid to fetch bottled water for us and later, I was able to get downstairs to reception and leave a message for the Cosmos rep to call. No one came.

On our third day, we looked shocking, yet managed to get up and go outside. We met up with another English couple, who looked to be in a similar fragile predicament. They too had been ill in bed. We sat in the shade by the pool, slowly coming round. By the fourth day, we began to eat a little and we decided to hire a car. We shared the cost between the four of us and John drove.

He took us up Mount Teide, where we were above the clouds and it was bitterly cold. He parked the car and we continued by cable-car, our ears popping en-route, and then walked to the summit. The air was thin and smelt of sulphur. A few breaks appeared in the clouds, through which we could see right across the island, which was beautiful, apart from its black sand beaches.

The image we had seen in the brochure was the only golden sand beach on the island, at the resort where we were staying. The north of the island was green and covered in trees that swayed gently in the breeze. Towards the south lay a vast and barren landscape.

The ten days were almost over and we had seen a small part of the world other than our homeland. Our tummy troubles settled down, and although we both had a nice tan, we vowed never to return to Tenerife.

On our flight home, over an hour into the journey, the skies were clear. Looking far below us, we could see miles and miles of golden sandy beaches. We asked the hostess where it was.

'Just a minute, I'll ask the captain.' A few minutes later, she returned from the cockpit.

'The Algarve, Portugal,' she said.

'That's where we'll go next year,' said John as he took hold of my hand.

I looked down at my suntanned arms and legs and couldn't wait to see Dave.

10

We made a quick call at Mum and Dad's before going to the Crown. I gave Dad a pack of duty-free tobacco and Mum the tablecloth and some Birds of Paradise flowers which hadn't travelled very well and didn't like the change of climate. They thanked us and gave us a hug and a kiss, and said how well we looked with our suntans. Promising to see them on Sunday, we dashed off to work.

Jo was getting married and was coming over this Sunday as she wanted to know if John would give her away. Dad couldn't do it, owing to his poor health. She had got engaged last Christmas and none of us had met Brian, her fiancé, who wanted to do the right thing and ask Dad for Jo's hand in marriage. He too was a teacher and had recently been made head at a school in Wolverhampton, where they were both teaching. I was looking forward to catching up with Jo again. It was three years since we had last met.

Try as I might, I couldn't get thoughts of Dave out of my head and people began to notice my lack of concentration. They assumed it was because I had stopped smoking, which I didn't find too difficult during the day, as neither John nor Dave smoked. The worst times were when I was working at the Crown. I found it relatively easy to refuse when offered a cigarette. It was much more difficult when the bar was busy and friends, while lighting their own, would light one for you and place it in the ashtray. That was when the real temptation kicked in. Yet, as each hour and day passed, my reserve became stronger.

I wanted to trim Dad's hair before his meeting with Brian. The following day, while John went to Bramall Lane to watch the match, I caught the bus to Owlerton. The journey wasn't too slow as there was only a reserve match at Hillsborough.

I looked out of the windows at the numerous advertisements on the billboards for the Labour Party, outnumbering the Conservative placards ten to one. The Labour ones depicted lit candles, reminding everyone of the three day working week. The Conservative posters, with extra-large letters, told everyone: "Labour isn't working".

Hillsborough Park came into view and I rang the bell to exit the bus.

I could tell that Mum had been out drinking again; her face was ruddy. I didn't comment.

'What do you think to Harold Wilson getting back in?' Dad said, as he knocked out his pipe and placed it on the mantelpiece, got up from his armchair and sat on a kitchen chair.

'Makes no difference to us, Dad, whoever's in.'

Mum gave me a disgusted look. She hated the fact that I didn't vote. 'Women died to get you the vote, and you can't be bothered to use it.'

'Perhaps their needs were greater than mine.' I took the scissors from my handbag.

'You have it too easy, that's your trouble,' she added, the colour in her face rising.

'Mum, don't stress yourself. What difference does it make to such as John and I? We don't have family allowance, we don't draw a pension, and we don't have supplementary benefit. We work hard and pay our way, like you and Dad always have.'

'You might live to regret saying that,' she said, as she took the bottle of Camp coffee from the kitchen cabinet.

'Is Auntie Doris alright?' I quickly changed the subject.

'Same as ever, smokes like a chimney, hair a different colour every week.'

'Well, at least she's not boring.'

'Ian's home,' she said, while making a coffee for herself and Dad. 'Do you want one?'

'No thanks,' I replied, tucking Dad's collar into his shirt. 'Where is Ian?'

'Hasn't got up yet.' She stirred two spoonfuls of sugar into Dad's coffee.

'What? The lazy so and so. I'll get him up.' I put down my scissors and ran upstairs into the back bedroom, which had belonged to all of us in turn. The room reeked of stale beer and cigarette smoke.

'Get up, you lazy sod,' I said, pulling the covers off him. 'It's three in the afternoon.'

He mumbled something and pulled the covers back over his head.

'Look at you, you're a disgrace. You've still got last night's clothes on.' I pulled back the covers and threw them on the floor. Then I pulled the curtains open and banged the window open with so much force, it shook the sashes.

He turned over slowly, forced open bloodshot eyes and tried to focus on the bedside table.

'It stinks like a brewery in here.' I pulled the cigarette packet and lighter away from his reach.

He sat up, yawned, scratched his head and then his crotch.

'Uhh, it's you.' His eyes were dazzled by the bright light from the window. He fumbled along the edge of the bedside table and then under his pillow. 'Have you moved my cigs?'

His eyes found the clock. 'Fuckin' 'ell, is that the time? I haven't put my bets on.' He stumbled out of bed. 'Jack, do us a favour, nip to the bookies and put us me bets on.'

'Get lost,' I said and went back downstairs.

'Hasn't he got a job yet?' I said to Mum and sat down in a chair.

'No, he's waiting till summer shutdown in the works and then he's going descaling chimneys and furnaces.'

'Working at the dog track didn't last long, did it? And who's keeping him in the meantime?' I said, crossing my legs and drumming my fingers on the table.

'Oh, that don't matter, love. He'll pay his board when he gets a job.' Mum tried to hide her face.

Dad gave a sarcastic grunt and stared towards the window.

'The more you let him get away with it, the more he's likely to do it. Dad, are you listening?' I shouted.

'It's not up to me, love, it's up to your mother, she sees to the housekeeping.' He didn't look at me while he replied.

'Oh, so you're just going to sit there and accept it, huh?'

He shrugged his shoulders. I stood up.

'Come on, let's get this hair cut,' I snatched the towel off the hook and picked up my scissors.

'Don't fret about it, love. It's nothing to do with you,' Mum chipped in.

I draped the towel round Dad's neck.

'You wouldn't let me go a week without paying my board,' I snapped.

'You mind where you're going with them scissors, waving them about like that,' said Dad.

I pushed his head forward. 'I even had to pay while I was away on holiday.'

'What's all the shouting about?' said Ian as he entered the room.

'It's about you,' I snapped. 'It's about time you found a proper job and paid your way.'

Dad remained quiet; he was aware that I was annoyed and had a pair of scissors at the back of his neck. Mum just shook her head.

Ian rinsed his face under the tap, gave it a quick wipe with the tea-towel, then picked his cigarette off the draining board and took a long drag.

'Ian,' said Mum, snatching the tea-cloth from him. 'How many times have I to tell you? Don't use the tea-towel.'

'Don't go on about it, Jack,' said Ian, as he looked around for the hand and face towel that was around Dad's neck. 'I've got a job coming up for the summer and...'

I cut him off. 'Oh yes, well, what about now?'

'Listen, know-it-all, what I earn over the summer working away is more than I could earn around here all year.'

'Ha,' I laughed. 'Don't give me that bullshit, Ian. With the amount you drink, smoke and gamble, there'll be nothing left by the time you get back.'

'Ouch!' Dad jumped as I nicked his ear.

I pushed his shoulders. 'And you shut up moaning or I'll cut the other one.'

~

I told John about it later at the Crown.

'You shouldn't get involved, Jack,' he said. 'Ian's not going to change and your parents have always spoilt him – and they're not going to change either.'

We broke off our conversation to serve customers who had just arrived.

'A pint of best and a snowball please. I see your team did well today, John, did you go?'

'Yes, it was a good game, Jim. Currie played well. Did you go?' John filled the pint glass and checked for clarity. 'Here you are, Jim, first one off – it's on the house.'

'Thanks, John. Nah, couldn't go. Had to go shopping with the missus.' He looked down at his pretty wife, dressed in her Saturday best, and hair set with recently removed rollers. Tweed perfume filled the area. They sat on stools in front of the bar and lit cigarettes. I could have snatched it out of her mouth.

'Help yourself, Jackie, or have you still stopped?'

I looked at the packet and moved nearer.

'Thanks, but no thanks, Irene, I'll not renege now.' I added a cherry on a cocktail stick to the snowball I had just made.

'Do you feel any better for it?' she asked.

'Well, no, I don't feel any different and I haven't put on any weight as everyone said I would.'

'Give it time,' she replied.

64

More supporters came in. There had been less talk of football since England had failed to qualify for the World Cup.

'England needs Don Revie as Manager,' I said. To which both sets of supporters closed ranks and showed obvious signs of disapproval at the thoughts of a Leeds United member managing England.

'Just wait and see – it'll surprise me if he's not the next England Manager.'

Saturday evenings were beginning to get back to normal, as the Sheffield Wednesday "away" supporters arrived. Harmless banter passed between the customers as rival followers of the two Sheffield clubs came in. As voices became raised and good humour prevailed, it wasn't long before it was like a regular Saturday. The pub filled up.

'There's only one United,' I said in a loud voice. The crowd hushed and stared. 'And that's Leeds.' I pulled my Leeds United scarf from under the counter and waved it the air.

Beer mats were thrown at me and I was booed and hissed.

'Rubbish,' they called and laughed. 'How do you put up with that, John?'

'She's not with me.' He grinned and carried on serving.

'Revie's team – Bremner, Hunter, Clarke, Jones, Charlton, Bates…' I shouted. But they cut me off.

'John, she's your missus, control her.'

John just laughed. 'Not likely, mate. I don't want strangling with a Leeds United scarf.'

I raised the scarf above my head with both hands and began singing 'We are the Champions', and walked into the tap room, laughing. I turned my head and looked back around the corner.

'And Giles, Jordan, Madeley…' I ducked as a beer mat whizzed past my head.

I waited a few minutes for the excitement to die down. The tap room was quiet; very few used that room at the weekend now the houses had been demolished and the steelworks had closed, or moved to out of town areas. I looked in the mirror at the back of the bar and tidied my hair before returning to the lounge.

Dave stood at the bar.

11

I tossed and turned during the night. I could feel the heat coming into my face again at the thought of him. I had worked too long behind the bar for any man to make me blush like I had last night, and I was unsure whether John had noticed it or not.

I had only seen Dave briefly since my return from Tenerife and had only seen him in the daytime, mostly in his work clothes. Tonight he looked more handsome than ever.

'Hello, have a good holiday?' he said when I appeared from the other room, the Leeds scarf put away.

As Dave spoke, John was pulling him a pint. John looked at Dave, and then me.

My breath caught in my throat and my colour began to rise. Luckily, a chap who was walking away from the bar with three pints grasped between his hands, nodded.

'I wouldn't talk to her, mate…Leeds supporter.' He winked at Dave, then at me.

'So am I, mate,' replied Dave, hands in jacket pockets, his eyes never leaving mine.

The bloke looked him up and down and walked off.

'Getting some right weirdos in 'ere lately,' he muttered.

Dave never flinched; he shrugged his shoulders and grinned.

'Get one for yourself and Jackie,' he said as John placed the pint on the counter.

'John, this is Dave, the plumber who fixed the sink,' I said, finding my voice, my facial tones now returning to normal.

'I'm alright just now, thanks,' said John, politely refusing a drink, his blue eyes dark.

'I'll have half please,' I chipped in. 'Fair return for mugs of tea, eh?'

John didn't look at me or Dave. He pulled half a bitter and placed it on the bar. Dave handed over a pound note and John gave me a strange look as he turned towards the till. John handed him his change and moved to serve someone else. I sometimes wondered if he had sixth sense.

'I'll just collect some glasses.' I went round to the front of the bar. I wanted to get a closer look. He was the tallest man standing, wearing a brown leather zipped-front bomber jacket and dark brown flares. His platform shoes were not too high, giving him an overall height of six-five.

Some of the women nudged each other.

'Who's the big guy, Jackie?' one asked as I neared the table. I shrugged my shoulders.

'He's new,' another said.

'Wouldn't mind going a round or two with him!' one of the other women said. 'I'm going to get another drink while he's still at the bar.'

Other women glanced and proffered weak smiles at the tall, handsome stranger.

I collected the empties and placed them on the bar, where John moved them to the sink.

'Cheers,' I said when I was back behind the bar. I took a drink from my glass.

'Cheers,' replied Dave. He lifted his glass and took a long drink, then licked the foam from his top lip. 'Good pint,' he commented. The pint glass looked like a half- pint glass in his hand.

'What brings you in here, then?' I was beginning to feel more confident – and without a cigarette too.

'My legs,' he replied.

'Silly question!' I laughed and broke off to serve someone else. I glanced over as Dave turned to look around the pub. His dark blond hair fell slightly over the top of his raised collar, sideburns down to his jaw line.

The beer spilled over the top of the glass.

'Oops! Sorry.' I pulled another top on the pint. I finished serving and went back to talk to Dave.

'I'm with Big Dave,' he continued. 'He's gone to see someone across the road in the Gardeners Rest. When I saw this place, I remembered you saying it was where you worked, so I thought I'd call in. Nice place – are you and John taking it over?'

'Yes, the owners are semi-retired,' I replied.

He took a long pull on his beer.

'The tan suits you,' he said, as The Three Degrees singing 'When Will I see You Again' came on the juke box. 'Great selection of records, too,' he added.

'Yes, I choose them.' I felt myself blushing again. John glanced over.

'I'd better get serving or I'll be in trouble.'

'Yes, I'd better be going too – otherwise Dave'll wonder where I've got to.'

'Where are you off to – down town?' I asked and moved to serve another customer.

'Probably, and finish in Baileys.' He drank the rest of his pint.

You can't, I wanted to scream as he turned to leave.

'See you around,' he winked. 'See you, John.' He made his way from the bar and didn't look back. He had taken part of me with him.

John looked for my reaction to his departure and nodded towards the customers.

~

Another night spent tossing and turning. I was tired when I finally awoke. A cup of tea on the bedside table had gone cold. I dressed and sauntered into the kitchen.

'Didn't want to wake you, love,' said John as he took the cup from me and emptied it down the sink. He'd taken the bacon, sausage, black pudding and eggs out of the fridge and placed them by the side of the cooker, then slid the plates in the top to warm.

The Sunday paper dropped through the letter box.

'Don't do me any black pudding, Jack, and only one egg,' he said as he went to the door to collect the newspaper. 'You didn't get any more of that sausage, did you? The one that tasted fishy.' He looked at the front page.

'No I didn't. I told the butcher about it though – he just said no one else had complained.' I placed a knob of lard in the frying pan. 'It's what they feed the pigs on nowadays. Factory farming – anything goes – fish waste, animal waste – anything.'

'I thought we'd have a run out to Castleton this afternoon.' He put the kettle on to boil and placed two spoonfuls of tea in the pot.

'We can't – we're going over to Mum's to see Jo and her new bloke.' I added the rashers of bacon to the frying pan and placed it on the hob.

'Oh well, some other time then. I'd forgotten about them coming over.'

~

Jo had kept in touch with Mum through occasional letters. I wondered if she knew that Mum had started drinking. It was late Sunday afternoon when we arrived; she was talking to Mum in the kitchen. There was an obvious hush as we entered.

'Not talking about me, are you?' I said, and went over and gave them both a hug. 'Come on then, where's this feller of yours?'

She pushed her hair to one side. It was still long, mousy-blonde, and parted down the middle, a typical student hairstyle.

'He's in the room, talking to Dad.'

'Poor lad, I bet he's been dreading it. John did when he asked Dad if he could marry me. Scared to death he was.'

'I think your dad would have asked John if he had left it much longer,' said Mum.

Jo and I laughed.

'I see you're still not wearing make-up, Jo.'

'Brian says I don't need it.'

'Ooooh! Get you,' I said, sounding like Auntie Doris.

Brian came into the kitchen.

'I'm glad that's over with,' he said, wiping his forehead with a clean hankie. I wasn't sure if that was genuine or an act.

'I told you there was nothing to be afraid of. Dad would have been more scared than you,' said Jo, before introducing us.

Brian was about five ten, the same as John but with mousy blond hair and blue eyes. He was quite attractive. He spoke softly, with a well-educated voice. As I listened to him, I realised that Jo no longer spoke with a Sheffield accent.

We talked of wedding plans and John said he would be pleased to give her away for the same reasons my cousin Len gave me away. Dad was certainly not up to it, although, he would sign the register as he had for me.

'Where are you having the reception?' I asked, excited and wanting to be involved.

'We are only having a small do at The Horse and Jockey, then going straight on honeymoon.'

'The Horse and Jockey, you'll not get many in there.' I pulled a face.

'It'll be big enough for us.' She was unconcerned by my reaction.

'But Jo, you only get married once. If you're having a church wedding with all the trimmings, you've got to have a proper reception.'

'Jack, I no longer know my relations, I have been away for so long and never kept in touch. It would be an unnecessary expense.'

'Jo, it doesn't have to cost a fortune. I'll ask Arnie and Kitty at the Crown how much they would charge. John and I would work that evening so they wouldn't have to pay out for extra bar staff.'

'Jack – it was different for you. You were going into a council flat, Brian and I are buying our own house and need a deposit.'

'What's wrong with living in a council flat until you've got enough for a deposit? The rents are reasonable.'

She didn't reply.

'You might as well just go the registry office then. Why bother with a church wedding?'

Her eyes darkened. 'I want to get married in God's house. That's why.'

'Whhaat?'

Mum, Brian and John kept quiet during our conversation, which was now heading towards an argument.

'For God's sake, Jo, you're beginning to sound like Mum.'

Mum stood up. 'Now that's enough. Jo will have the wedding she wants. It's not your choosing.' She was angry and staring at me. 'And, you – I've told you before about taking the Lord's name in vain in this house.'

The door opened and Ian staggered in, smelling of too much alcohol.

'What's this then – family gathering? Who's died?'

'No one yet. Could be you if you don't smarten yourself up,' I said.

'Chuff me, hark at Billy Graham,' he said, lighting a cigarette. 'You must be the other unfortunate.' He looked at Brian and then at John.

No one answered, yet Brian thought it funny.

'Well, as it's a nice family get together, who's going to lend me a tenner?'

'Ian, clear off,' I said and looked away.

He gave me a Nazi salute, belched and went upstairs.

~

John and I talked about the meeting with Jo and Brian later when we were at the Crown. It was early, and the Sunday nighters hadn't arrived.

'I can't believe she's not having a reception, can you? And fancy going camping in France on honeymoon.' I was cutting up slices of lemon on the back of the counter.

I shook some miniature sword cocktail sticks into my hand. 'They learn how to speak French at University,' I added.

'Didn't you?'

I looked at him. He was grinning.

'According to your mother, you did!'

'Oh yes, *Parlez-vous Francais,* and that's my limit,' I said, laughing.

I took some glacé cherries from the jar and placed them on sticks in a small glass bowl.

'What did you think to Brian?'

'He's okay, I suppose, clever.'

'He should be, he's a headmaster,' I replied. 'He's a bit young for a headmaster, don't you think? They didn't have them that age when I was at school. They were all old fogeys.'

'That's because we're getting older.'

'Don't say that – we'll never survive to get old with the reckless life we live.'

I thought about how different Jo and I were and the different things we both wanted from life, and what she saw in Brian.

'I found it difficult to converse with him though. Did you notice that, John? They seem to think on a different wave-length.'

'That's university for you.' He wiped the bottles of Guinness and placed them on the shelf.

'It's as if he couldn't give a direct reply. He had to think things through before answering, and even then he looked worried in case it wasn't the right answer.'

'Probably years of studying has that effect on you,' John moved the empty bottle crate and went to serve the first customer.

I thought again about Jo. She too was serious all the time; no sense of humour. Didn't know any jokes. Didn't laugh at the ones I told. Ah well, I thought, if that's what university does for you I'm glad I went to the University of Life. I bit into a cherry; strange how sweet things appealed now I'd stopped smoking.

Chapter 12

I had never made love to anyone other than John, who had never disappointed me. But now, I found I needed more. I was unsure as to what, apart from dreaming of rampant sex with my friend the plumber. It was only a matter of time before temptation became stronger than our reserve.

On Monday, after seeing Jo and Brian, the morning sky was clear blue and the sun was shining. After a miserable spring, summer was on its way. The view into the park was extra beautiful. The recent rain had saturated the ground, giving the park an almost tropical feel.

I opened the windows. The different scents rose with the steam from the grassed areas. I looked down on the trees, which were in full leaf, in all shades of green. On the rhododendrons which lined the path, buds were bursting into flowers of blue, purple, yellow and orange. I was overwhelmed with a desire to capture it on paper. I hadn't painted, apart from decorating, for a long time. A few Christmases ago, John had bought me a set of watercolours and paper; a sketchpad and charcoal sticks, my favourite media.

I was sketching when Dave arrived.

'What are you drawing? I thought you only painted,' he said as he came and stood close behind me, looking over my shoulder at my drawing; then over my head into the park. He smelled shower-fresh, with masculine undertones.

'I prefer drawing to painting, actually.'

'Woman of mystery, eh?'

'There's a lot of things you don't know about me,' I said, still facing the park.

'I know how good you looked on Saturday night.' He lowered his head to my ear, his voice deep and husky.

My heart skipped a beat and a sent a thrill through my body and down to my pelvis. Ashamed of what I might do, I carried on sketching. He must have sensed my reluctance to comment as a rejection.

'Do you want a cuppa?'

'Water for me please,' I replied. 'It's too warm for tea. I'll do it in a minute.'

'You carry on. I'll make it.' He went into the kitchen, whistling.

Five minutes later, he returned with a mug of tea and a glass of water. I put down the charcoal and turned to face him.

'Carry on,' he said. 'Don't let me stop you.' He lounged across the settee.

I took a drink of the water and looked at his face and firm square jaw.

'Hold it right there.' I turned to a new page on my pad.

'Hold what?' He grinned. 'Can't I drink my tea?'

I began sketching. 'Yes, of course, just go back into the same position.'

This was the first time I had looked at him and not looked away. His eyes, dark and expectant, held mine as my hand moved across the paper. The window was slightly open and the warm summer breeze filtered in with distant sounds of a city on the move. The soothing tones of The Carpenters singing 'Yesterday Once More' came over on Radio 1.

His image began to take shape; my hand moving faster of its own accord, copying every inch of his masculinity: the contrast between the taut outline of his neck as it disappeared into the softness of his shirt collar. The shape of his shoulders and tightness of the shirt sleeves across his biceps. His chest, that rose and fell with each deep breath. I captured it, along with the taut stomach muscles.

74

My hand and eye moved in unison, working away across and down his body to his jeans, until I saw the bulge. My hand stalled. He knew I had seen it, and made no move to shift his position, and this time, I didn't look away.

The room filled with silence as the Carpenters came to the end of their song. The mellow tones of Bobby Goldsboro followed, singing his hit 'Summer (The First Time)'.

As the singer remembered a hot afternoon of seduction, we stared at each other; the sensual words generating our repressed emotions. Neither of us moved.

The song continued. My eyes never left his as I stood and placed the drawing pad on the table. I moved towards him and reached out my hand. He covered my hand with his and stood up. Stepping back, I brought him towards me and led him to the bedroom. I licked my lips and left them open.

It was finally happening, after weeks of dreaming of this moment. He took me in his arms. I closed my eyes as he pulled me towards him. The strength I had admired for so long took my breath away as he held me close. My body thrilled with sensations that I didn't want to end.

I felt his lips close over mine; his body pressed closer as his hands slid over my back and hips. Our tongues entwined, we fell onto the bed, passion deepening.

My body shook with a need I didn't know I possessed as his hands; large, yet so gentle, caressed my body. He raised himself and removed his shirt. I gasped: the long-awaited vision of his naked chest filled my eyes.

Reaching up, I pulled him towards me. I wanted him so much. This sight of his well-rounded shoulders inflamed me more as his hands and arms wrapped and folded around my body.

I sat up and unfastened my blouse; it slid down over my arms. I leaned back and watched his face as he looked at my small breasts, covered with a white lace bra. I leaned forward and unfastened it, allowing it to fall. His eyes darkened as he reached for me. Raising my

75

hips, I slid my jeans over my thighs. Unashamedly, I lay, wearing just my white lace panties.

The muted tones of the song filtered through the dividing wall.

He stood up and unfastened his belt, unzipped his fly and eased his jeans over his thighs, taut leg muscles flexed as he moved from one foot to the other. His erection stood proud as he removed his boxers. I pulled him on top of me and we kissed again, our tongues turning, exploring each other.

He tasted of warmth and love, of passion and desire, strength and yet tenderness. He stroked my thighs until his fingers found the edge of my panties and then my groin. His thumb slid beneath the lace, caressing and stroking, until he found it. My breath caught in my throat and I raised my hips up to him as he stroked gently with his thumb. Never before had I felt desire like this.

'Fill me,' I said.

~

We lay together, exhausted, my head in the crook of his arm. An invisible barrier had been crossed, and as we stared at each other, we both knew this was something more than a quick fling.

I pulled him back on top of me. I had found my soulmate. I clung to him, not wanting to let him go. Then I suddenly became overcome with guilt. This should have happened weeks ago, before deep emotions had entered into it. Then, perhaps by now it would have petered out and our lives would have returned to normal. Now it was too late. We were already committed and deeply in love. Our act today served only to confirm it.

~

We saw each other every day, except weekends. Sometimes just for a few minutes, and those minutes were so precious.

'Come and live with me, Jack?' he said one day.

'Dave, as much as I want to, I can't leave John. He's a good man and he loves me. And you're still married, with a family.'

'I love you, Jack, more than anything else in the world. I can't stand it, having to leave you every time we meet.'

We were in bed, basking in the afterglow. 'No you don't, Dave, you're just saying that.' I turned and looked at the bedside clock.

'Don't say that, Jack, please.' He pulled me towards him, crushing me in his arms. His chin rested on my head. I knew he meant every word he said.

'And I love you, Dave, but two wrongs don't make a right.' I stroked his back with my free arm. 'Too many people are going to get hurt. I can't face that.' I was overcome with guilt again; a cheat. I hated myself.

'Look, Dave, you've got to go. The time's getting on.' I pulled my arm away from entwining his back.

He held me tighter.

'No, not unless you promise you'll live with me.'

'Stop it, Dave. I can't breathe.'

He let me go and stroked my hair.

'I'm sorry, Jack, you're the last person I'd want to hurt.'

I rolled over and sat on the edge of the bed. I couldn't hurt him either; I loved him too much. I turned and grabbed hold of him with a strength only an animal could possess.

Chapter 13

I received a letter from the hospital, stating that they'd had a cancellation and I could have my tonsillectomy the following week. I phoned the Crown and told them straight away. Then I went to town and bought a new nightie, a longer version of my Babydolls, in powder blue instead of bright red, and a matching dressing gown and fluffy slippers. With these and a boxy train-case filled with toiletries, John took me to the Royal Infirmary a week later.

I checked in and was taken to the ward, where I was shown to a bed. The nurse closed the curtains while I undressed, put on my nightie and climbed into bed. John watched me, then folded my day clothes and put them in a bag to take home. He kissed me, held me tight in a final hug, and left.

The following morning, I was taken to the operating theatre. Someone stuck a needle in the back of my hand and told me to count backwards from a hundred.

'Ninety-nine, ninety-eight, ninety-seven…do I have to count right down to…'

~

I heard the sound of female voices and a trolley's squeaky wheels.

'Jacqueline, Jacqueline, wake up.' Someone was shaking me.

'Here, drink this,' said a nurse who was about the same age as me. She helped me to sit up.

I looked around at all the other beds; I was back on the ward. Then the pain seared in my throat and I felt sick. I looked up at the nurse and clutched my neck.

'Drink it, Jacqueline, it will ease the pain.'

I looked at the thick white liquid in a small glass.

'Do I have to? I can't swallow.'

'Try, you'll feel much better after.'

I took the glass from her. The contents looked like and had the consistency of condensed milk. It didn't taste like it. I wanted to scream as the thick liquid rasped my throat.

'Ugh, what is it?'

'Aspirin – it's to put a coating on your throat, before you eat,' she said, making sure I drank every drop.

'Eat! I couldn't eat anything, honest.'

She smiled as she took the glass from me and walked away. The pain in my throat was terrible. I was just snuggling down when she came back, carrying a bowl of cornflakes and a spoon.

'Sit up, Jacqueline.' Another nurse joined her.

My eyes were fixed on the bowl in her hand as I slowly sat up. Someone in the bed opposite moaned and shouted for a nurse. Another nurse went over and pulled the curtains around the bed. The woman moaned again.

'You're not going to like this, Jacqueline, but you have to eat.' She held the bowl and spoon towards me.

'What? You're joking,' I croaked.

She didn't move. She raised her eyebrows and nodded.

'It's to slough your throat,' the other nurse said.'

'There's no milk on them.' I shook my head. 'I thought it was ice-cream we were supposed to have?'

They laughed.

'Come on, Jacqueline, it's just this once. If you don't slough, your throat will heal with adhesions.'

Reluctantly, I took the bowl and spoon from her.

'Okay,' I said and waited for them to leave. But they didn't. They waited until every last cornflake had been taken from the dish, and then I was given a cup of tea.

~

John came to see me that evening on his way to the Crown. He gave me a kiss and a gentle hug, holding me as if I was a glass bauble. We didn't talk much – I was tired and needed to sleep. The nurse told him it was perfectly natural and that I would be much improved by tomorrow.

Tomorrow arrived and I did feel better. My throat was still painful, yet I managed to go across the ward to the toilet, wash my face and comb my hair and also to give a urine sample.

Two o'clock and the ward doors opened. The nurse came over.

'You have a visitor, Jacqueline. Do you want to sit in your chair?' She helped me out of bed and handed me my dressing gown. 'It's your boyfriend.' She gave me a cheeky grin.

'Boyfriend! I'm too old for boyfriends,' I replied.

'Not this one!' She made sure that I was well covered before leaving. Didn't want visitors getting ideas, I suppose.

I stood up as Dave came over, a smile on his face as big as the man himself. He was carrying a bunch of deep red roses, which he placed on the bed while he gave me a big hug.

'Ouch, careful, I'm not up to rough stuff yet.' I grinned.

'Who isn't?' he said and began closing the bedside curtain.

'Stop it, Dave. People are looking.'

'So? It's because they've never seen anyone as beautiful as you.'

I began to laugh and then cringed.

'Don't make me laugh, it hurts.' I sat back down as Dave went to find a chair.

The nurse who had forced the cornflakes down me came over. 'What beautiful flowers – lucky you,' she said. 'I'll get you a vase.'

Dave returned, sat down and held my hands in his, his eyes full of love.

'I've missed you, Jack.' He raised my hands to his lips and kissed them.

'I've only been gone two days, Dave. I've missed you too.' I looked at the roses. 'Thanks, Dave, they're beautiful.'

The nurse came back with a glass vase containing water and gave it to Dave.

He stood up. 'Thanks,' he said, handing it back. 'I'm no good at this sort of thing.'

The nurse removed the wrapping from the flowers and placed them in the vase.

'What a deep scent they have.' She took a deep breath as she placed them on the bedside table.

'As deep as my love,' said Dave, still holding my hands and looking straight at me.

'My, you've got it bad, haven't you?' said the nurse as she straightened her apron and walked away.

Dave didn't stay long; he had to return to the depot. John worked too far away for afternoon visits. When all the visitors had gone, I moved the flowers onto the windowsill, which was between me and the elderly lady in the next bed.

Chapter 14

I was discharged within the week. Dad's hair was due for cutting, what bit he had left: nowadays, it was more like tidying his neck, nostrils and ears.

Turning down the old familiar street, I could smell hops. The air smelled the same as it did near the Crown when Stones were brewing. It became stronger as I continued walking, and when I entered the house, it was like walking into a brewery. Passing the bottom of the stairs, I could see demi-johns containing cloudy brown liquid, standing to one side of the first three steps.

'What's going on here?' I said to Dad, although I didn't need to ask.

'It's your mother, she's gone bloody daft. Brewing her own barley wine, she is.'

'I can tell that, you can smell it at the top of the street. Where is she, anyhow?'

'Across the yard at the lav,' Dad replied.

I looked in the pantry. There was a white fermentation bucket, a siphon, thermometer and hydrometer, a fermenter with an airlock, a large boiling pot, bottles and caps. I slammed the door and went back to the staircase, lifted one of the demi-johns and took it over to the sink.

The door opened.

'What do you think you're doing?' She screamed, ran towards me and grabbed my arms, her face red and angry.

'I'm getting rid of this lot,' I said, equally furious.

'Don't you dare touch them, they're mine.' She was pulling at me with all her strength.

'Stop it, Mum. Look at you, you're a disgrace, you stink of alcohol. The street stinks of it.'

Dad stood in the background, agitated, and rubbing the blood blisters on his head.

She clawed my arms.

'You can't come back here and do this to me. You've left. I'll change the locks so you can't get in. You drink – I've never said anything about that, have I?'

'I drink – yes I drink – not to the extent that I need to brew my own.'

'You don't have to. You've got it on tap at that pub you work in.'

'Come and sit down, Margaret,' Dad finally said. 'You'll give yourself a heart attack.'

Dad was getting upset. 'I'll come back later, Dad.' I left the demi-john by the sink and stormed back up the street.

~

I told John about what I had seen.

'Something's got to be done about her, I don't know what. Do you think if I went to see her doctor, he would help?'

'I don't know, Jack. Perhaps – it might be worth a call.'

'I'll see if I can get an appointment to see him, tomorrow.'

The door opened and the first customers of the evening came in.

'Well, look who it is! Welcome strangers – Terry and Shirl!' We made a fuss of each other. It had been about a year since we'd last seen them.

'What are you having?' said John. He took a pint glass from under the counter. He pulled a pint for Terry while I poured a fruit juice for Shirl.

'You two are looking really well,' she said.

'Thanks, you're looking good yourselves. What have you been up to?'

'Lots – you first. When's it due?'

'When's what due?' I replied, the smiles slowly disappearing from our faces.

'The baby. You are pregnant, aren't you?' Shirley's eyes widened. John and Terry looked at each and shrugged; girl-talk.

'Ye gods, Shirl, not to my knowledge. I've just had my tonsils out, if that's anything to go on.'

'Looks like I'm the first to know.' She took a drink of juice and grinned, looking quite pleased. I was still shocked by her words; she must have seen it.

'Jackie, you just look so fit and well, you've gained weight and only a pregnant woman can have a glow like that. What do you think, Terry?'

'She's always looked good to me,' he replied.

I convinced her I wasn't pregnant and took a long drink of my beer while they relayed their happenings. I couldn't help wondering. Shirl wasn't the only one who had recently commented on my well-being and glowing aura, which I thought was due to having my tonsils out, stopping smoking and being deeply in love.

My thoughts deepened. Could I be pregnant? No, of course not. I was on the pill.

I excused myself to go to the toilet and leaned against the cubicle door. When was my last period? That wouldn't tell me. I'd had false periods because of the pill. Convinced I was safe, I opened the door, washed my hands and looked into the mirror.

Oh no! The operation! Before I went into hospital, I'd had to stop taking it for a while. I shook my head and looked down into the sink. If I was pregnant, it might not be John's.

~

I met Dave in The Blue Ball the following day. It was a city centre pub, where we were unlikely to know anyone.

We were standing as close together as was publicly acceptable, near one of the pillars, secretly holding hands.

'Some old friends of ours came into the pub last night and she thought I was pregnant.' I looked at him, anxious to see what his reaction would be.

He grabbed me. 'Good. You'll make a marvellous mother.' His face was beaming.

I pushed him away. 'Dave, this is serious. What if I am?'

'You'll come and live with me, we'll have lots more and we'll live happily ever after.' He took me in his arms again.

This was Dave; couldn't be serious if he tried.

'Dave, look at me. It might not be yours.'

'Doesn't matter.' He hugged me to him.

I didn't think I could love him any more than I did now. At that moment, I could have run to the ends of the earth with him.

'Dave, be serious, for once.'

'I've never been more serious.' The grin had gone.

'Where would we live?'

'Doesn't matter. If you love someone, you'll live in a cardboard box with them.' He let go of me, took hold of my hand and took a drink from his glass.

I suddenly saw a flash of bright ginger hair coming towards us.

'Oh no!' I mumbled, knowing I couldn't look anywhere else. It was Auntie Doris, her eyes aglow with curiosity.

'Well, well! If it isn't our Jack-a-leen.'

Dave and I let go of each other's hands. Doris looked him up and down and then back at me.

'Hmm!' She stared, waiting for an answer.

'Auntie Doris, this is Dave, a friend of mine. Dave, this is Auntie Doris.'

'Hello, Auntie Doris,' he said. The grin had returned.

I shook my head as the grin spread across his face. He was so happy with my news, I feared he might say something to her.

She pursed her lips, smiled, and then looked from him to me.

'He works on our estate, he's a plumber. He put me a new sink in.' I picked up my glass of beer from the shelf and took a quick drink.

She looked up at Dave, who was head and shoulders above her.

'A plumber, eh? Well, you can come and fix my damp patch any day, big fella.'

Dave laughed. 'Sense of humour, eh? Must run in the family.'

'I said he's a plumber, not a plasterer.' I turned away and took another drink.

'Well he can come and look at me pipes, then.' She burst out laughing; so did I.

'It definitely runs in the family,' said Dave, finishing his pint. 'Same again?' He looked down at me and then at Auntie Doris. 'What are you having, Auntie Doris?'

'I'm with someone, thanks, but I'll not say no. Half for me as well, Dave.'

She said it as if she'd known him for years. Dave went to the bar and Auntie Doris took her cigarettes out of her pocket and took two from the packet.

'No thanks,' I said, as she handed one to me. 'I've stopped.'

'Never,' she said, looking surprised. 'Pity you can't find the will power to stop biting your nails as well,' she added, taking hold of my hand. She kept hold of it and looked around, then pulled me towards her. 'If you're playing with fire, mind you don't get burnt. John's a good lad and I'd hate to see him hurt,' she whispered and looked around again. 'Have your fling and settle back down. It's time you started a family, not an affair.'

She clutched my hand tighter and shook it to make sure I'd got the message, then let go and straightened up as Dave returned from the bar. The smile returned to her face.

'Cheers, Dave.' She sipped the foam off the top of the glass.

'What are you doing in here anyhow?' I said. 'I thought you only stayed around Hillsborough.'

She looked over to where she had been sitting. A man waved. She raised her glass to him and turned to me.

'I'm doing the same as you,' she replied, grinning. 'Only I'm not married.' She raised her eyebrows and walked away.

Chapter 15

I had to decide. John had given me an ultimatum. Stay or leave. Looking as terrible as I felt, I phoned Dave's depot and left a message for him to ring me.

I looked through the local paper to find a job; I had to go back to work full-time. Then I remembered I could be pregnant, and felt even worse.

I phoned Brook Street Bureau to see what they had available. Most of the vacancies were for temps and you needed typing abilities for that. Lynn and I had left our night-school classes when we were fifteen, because we had other things to do in the evenings. I regretted it now.

A knock came at the door. I knew it was Dave. I couldn't face him, looking like this.

'Jack, open the door. What's the matter?'

'It's John, he's found out,' I said, through the letter box.

'Open the door or I'll break it down.' He banged louder.

'No you won't.' Despite all my sadness, I suddenly wanted to laugh. This was Dave, the gentle giant. Why did he have this crazy effect on me? 'You'd be damaging council property.'

'That's okay, I'd have to come and repair it.' The door shook as he threw himself against it.

'No you wouldn't,' I shouted. 'They'd send a joiner.' I unlocked it.

He stepped inside and pulled me into his arms.

'Get off me, Dave.' I struggled to get out of his grip.

'No, not until you promise you'll not stop seeing me.'

'I can't, Dave. You know I can't. I'm staying with John.'

He let me go. 'Look at me, Jack.'

I couldn't. My face was such a mess. 'No, Dave. I don't want you seeing me like this.'

He lifted my head and placed his hands on my shoulders.

'Beautiful,' he said, as he pulled me closer and kissed me on the lips.

My arms went up around his neck and I held him close.

'Jack.' He lifted his head. 'Never leave me, please, I'm begging.'

'Don't say that, please, Dave.' His eyes were wet.

He took hold of the top of my arms.

'Look at me and tell me you never want to see me again.'

I looked up. I could barely see; my eyes were almost shut, swollen with crying.

'Dave, I…' I pulled his head down towards me and kissed him, long and hard.

He let me go, took hold of my hand and led me down the hall.

'Come on, you need a cup of tea.'

I wandered into the lounge and through bleary eyes, looked out into the park below. Was it only a few weeks since we'd declared our love, in a passionate embrace which I still tingled from? Dave came from the kitchen, carrying two mugs of tea.

'Here, drink this.' He placed it on the coffee table, came behind me and wrapped his arms around my waist. He rested his chin on the top of my head. We stood, looking out of the windows at the city on the move.

There was a knock on the door.

'I'll go,' said Dave.

I sat down and took a drink of tea as he went down the corridor.

'It's the old lady who lives in the corner flat. She says you haven't put her drops in,' he said when he came back.

I jumped up.

'I forgot. She recently had an eye removed and asked if I would put her drops in every morning.' I made a move towards the door.

'You stay there, I'll do it.'

'Dave, it's not very pleasant.'

'Shh. Drink your tea.'

I sat back. What on earth was I going to do?

After ten minutes, he returned.

'Job done,' he said, and took a drink. 'Argh, it's cold.' He pulled a face. 'It's still wet though,' he added, as he drank the remainder.

'Did you manage her drops?'

'Yeah, she lifted her patch and told me to open the closed eye as far as possible and put three drops in.'

'That's the hardest part. How much will it open?'

'She said she'd scream if I went too far.'

'I told her if she was going to be a problem patient, I'd put some flux in.'

'You never said that.'

'I did – she just laughed. She'd already told me her husband had been a plumber before he died, so she knew exactly what flux was.' He came and sat beside me. 'I'd sooner be looking after you though. Do you want some more tea, a slice of toast?'

'No thanks. Dave, we need to talk…'

'Never, Never Gonna Give Ya Up' came on the radio. Dave took me in his arms, looked into my eyes and sang along with Barry White. I nuzzled my head into his chest.

The song finished.

'Dave, I've got to get ready for work.' I pulled away from his arms and went to the bathroom. He followed.

'Jack…'

'Jesus! I can't go in looking like this,' I said as I looked in the mirror.

'Why don't you go back to bed? I'll ring the pub and tell them you can't get in.'

'You can't ring them.'

'Why not?'

'Because you can't, they don't know you.'

'I'll tell them I'm the doctor,' he laughed. 'Actually, an eye specialist.'

'Dave, don't do this to me, please. We have to part.'

'Look, you're too upset to talk and I've got to go. I've a job in the next block. I'll be back later. Do you want any shopping getting?' He went to the kitchen and looked in the fridge. 'There's not much in here, what are you having for tea?' he called.

I shook my head and went over to the fridge. He was right, the fridge was bare.

'I couldn't eat anything, Dave, so don't bother.'

'Okay, John will want his tea when he comes home, won't he?'

I was staring out of the kitchen window. I heard him open the cupboard door.

'You've got a few potatoes left and some carrots.'

I sighed and turned. 'Okay, get me a cauli and three lamb chops, and a couple of slices of lamb's liver, please. Don't get pig's liver, John doesn't like it.'

'I'll tell you what, I'll double the amount and I'll come for tea,' he said as he made his way to the door. 'Now go to bed. I'll see you later…And be up before I come back – or else!'

I leaned against the door. How could I possibly live without him? I picked up the phone and dialled the number for the Crown.

The key turned in the lock. The door opened and closed. I was dreading this moment. The hall cupboard door opened. I heard John change his shoes and then use the bathroom. I began to plate up.

'Decided to stay, then?' he said with cool indifference as he kissed my cheek.

I turned to face him. 'John, I'm sorry, I…'

He cut me off. 'I don't want to hear anything about it. You've decided to stay, so let that be the end of it.' A warning look was in his eyes. He turned and went into the lounge.

I finished plating up and carried the plates into the room. John switched on the TV and sat at the table.

Placing the plates on the mats, I sat down and pushed the food around my plate.

'I didn't go to the Crown this lunch-time – I couldn't go, looking like this.' He didn't reply; he didn't even look at me. 'I said I wouldn't be in tonight either.'

'I'll still be going.' He kept his head down, looking at his plate as he ate. He didn't want to be with me.

'John, would you rather I'd left?' My stomach trembled.

'I don't want to talk about it, Jack. You've made your choice.' He looked at me, his blue eyes cold as steel. He watched the rest of the news, then cleared the table.

'I'll do the dishes if you're going to the Crown,' I said as he ran the hot water for the dishes.

'I can still do them.' He washed and I wiped.

John showered and put on a clean shirt and trousers, then with a quick peck on my cheek, left for the Crown. I watched *Emmerdale Farm* and *Rising Damp*. The phone rang when I was on my way to bed.

'Is everything alright? Can you talk?'

'Yes. I might not have been able to.'

'I'll come up then.'

'No, Dave, don't. I'm just going to bed.'

'Good, give me five minutes.'

'Dave!' I shouted. 'I've got a blinding headache and need to sleep. I've just taken some aspirins.' My lips spoke the words, yet *come on up, I can't wait*, my heart said.

'Okay then, I'll leave you in peace. Did he say anything?'

'Not much, it was an awful atmosphere.'

'Tell me tomorrow – I'll see you in the morning. Love you.'

Chapter 16

The following morning, I rose early. John had already left for work. My face didn't look too bad. Carefully applied make-up concealed the puffiness.

I applied Mrs Ward's eye-drops and ran down the steps to the basement. Walking through the park on my way into town, I saw Dave's van parked by the Special School. I remembered him telling me he had a job there first thing this morning.

I stopped, not wanting him to see me. Children with learning difficulties were climbing all over him. He was laughing and playfully chasing them off as they came back for more. The teachers looked on, encouraging the youngsters to "get" him. It was hard to tell who was having most fun. When he was looking the other way, I ran past the playground fence.

I thought about him in a different way as I turned down Granville Road. I couldn't go with him: we led different lives. He had children of his own, and that's where he belonged, with them, and yet he was willing to give them up for me. I took a deep breath and continued into town.

~

I called into the staff bureaus; there was nothing suitable. I walked up to Holly Street, near the Grammar School where I had taken my art exam years ago and bought some A4 paper, carbon and copy paper. Next, I called into the library and borrowed a Pitman's College *Teach Yourself Touch-Typing* book. Now all I needed was a typewriter. I went home with new determination. Getting a full-time job would help.

'Jack, I'll not see you as much,' said Dave when I told him.

'We're not supposed to be seeing each other at all, Dave.' I didn't want a repeat performance of yesterday, so I held his hand.

'But Jack…'

'No buts, Dave. I've got to go back to full-time working.'

'Will you still see me?' He pulled me closer, crushing me in his arms.

'Let's see how it pans out.'

He gripped me tighter. I did want to see him, with all my heart I did. I dreaded the thought of not seeing him again, or his being with someone else.

'Yes, we'll have to be extra careful. Anyhow, I haven't got a job yet.'

'I love you, Jack. More than anything else in the world,' he whispered into my hair.

~

John came home at tea-time and I placed our meals on the table. He was quiet and gave me a slight peck on the cheek. There was an atmosphere you could cut with a knife. I couldn't live like this.

He washed the dishes and tidied away, then went into the living room to read the paper, which had just arrived.

'Pass me the ads section, please,' I said, while he was studying the back page. 'I want to see if there's a cheap typewriter for sale.' He looked up and passed me the pages. 'I've been to the bureaus today and the only suitable jobs are for shorthand typists, or clerk typists.'

'What's wrong with working in a shop again? You're good with money.'

'I don't want Saturday work again.'

~

The following day, he came home from work with a black Imperial typewriter.

'That's fab, John. Where did you get it from?' I was eager to start practicing.

'The Drawing Office – that's why it has a long carriage, they're replacing the old models with the new Remingtons.'

I took a sheet of paper; the blue carbon and copy paper and threaded the three sheets through the carriage, looked at the keys and tried to remember the little I had learned at night school. I began practicing: a, s, d, f, g, ; l, k, j, h, and then sentences and capitals: *The quick brown fox jumped over the lazy dog.*

Over and over I practiced and kept checking the copy paper to make sure I was hitting the keys hard enough. Before long, my wrists were aching and my fingertips were sore from the stiffness of the keys. Within a few days, I managed to achieve thirty words a minute. I needed to do better than that; most places required a minimum of fifty. I couldn't reach that without proper training, and the evening classes didn't start until September. I couldn't wait that long.

~

A few days later, the phone rang.

'Have you seen your dad lately?' The voice shouted. It was Mum; she sounded drunk. 'He's poorly, you know, what do you care…?'

'Mum, shut up shouting.' She was still rambling and I had to talk over her. 'Mum, calm down and tell me what's the matter. Mum, are you still there? Mum.'

The line was dead. She must have been in the phone box at the top of the street. I'd heard traffic in the background. I looked at the clock – nine-thirty. If I went now, I'd have time to call in before the lunch-time shift at the Crown.

~

She was slumped in her chair, fast asleep and snoring when I arrived, her face the colour of a freshly boiled lobster. I looked in the pedal-bin and saw two empty Gold Label bottles. I banged the lid back down.

'What's happened, Dad?' Dad sat in his chair, arms folded across his chest, the pipe bowl in one hand, the tip of the stem between his lips.

'Huh! Don't ask me,' he muttered, looking straight at the kitchen window. He couldn't see out; the nets were drawn.

'Well, who do I ask then?' I was getting angry.

He laughed slightly and shrugged his shoulders, eyes still fixed on the beyond.

I put my handbag on the table, went over to him and knelt down.

'Dad, are you alright?' I placed my hands on his knees; they were bony. He'd lost weight since I'd last seen him. 'Mum called me, she said you were ill.'

Mum gave a throaty snort, her head moved to one side and her mouth fell open.

Dad suddenly jumped and shook his head.

'Hello, love, what are you doing here?' He placed his pipe on the mantelpiece and stroked the bit of hair on the back of his head. 'Is it due for cutting already?'

'Dad, listen to me. Mum said you were ill.' My knees began to hurt so I sat on the chair arm.

'Oh it's nothing, love. Me chest's been playing up again and the doc want s me to go for some tests. Top and bottom of it is – when your time's up, it's up.'

'Don't talk like that, Dad.' I leaned towards him and kissed the top of his head. I suddenly realized that Dad was almost eighty-seven. I fought back the tears welling up inside. 'Come on, Dad, there's plenty of life left in you yet.' I gave him a cuddle.

He squeezed my hand.

'You'll not let them take me in hospital, will you, Jack? Promise me that.'

I looked into his tired eyes, the cataracts more evident.

'I promise, Dad.' I swallowed hard. 'Let's have a cup of coffee, eh?'

I was just getting up from the chair arm when a young blonde-haired woman walked past, towards the cooker.

'Hello,' she said and smiled when she saw me.

I was astounded. It wasn't the fact that she spoke with a foreign accent, it was that she was wearing no clothes.

She filled the kettle and turned towards me.

'Who are you?' she said, smiling sweetly.

I was still mesmerized. 'I'm Jack....'

'Ah, Billy Graham.' She laughed and tossed her head back; long blonde hair swept over her shoulders.

I suddenly came to my senses.

'Just a minute, who the bloody hell are you?'

'I am Ingrid, from Sweden – Ian's friend, do you want coffee too?'

I ran upstairs.

'Get out of bed, you lazy bugger.' I pulled the covers from his horny naked body. 'Get up and get out.'

'Uhh! Hi, Jack.' He reached for his cigs.

I knocked them out of his hand.

'Steady, hold on a minute, lass...'

'Never mind, *hold on lass*. Get out.' I pointed to the door.

The blonde came into the bedroom carrying two mugs of coffee. I bet she doesn't have to shave, I thought, as I saw the silky golden patch of pubic hair.

'And you, you get out as well.' I threw an item of clothing from the floor at her. 'I don't care how you behave at home. You're not at home now.'

I heard them laugh as I stormed out and down the stairs. Mum was still asleep in the chair. I kissed Dad on the cheek.

'I'll see you later Dad,' I said, and left.

I couldn't wait to get out of the madhouse.

Chapter 17

At least the conversation melted the ice between me and John somewhat when I related the story to him, later.

I continued to practice my typing; every spare moment I had. It also helped to take my mind off the pregnancy problem. For all my endeavours, I couldn't get past forty words a minute. I was beginning to despair, when I had a phone call from one of the bureaus. A vacancy had arisen at Globe and Simpson on West Street, for a typist/pricing clerk. There were no set typing speeds.

I arranged an interview, and then asked around and in the pub to find out more about the company. They were agents and distributors for Lucas and S.A.V.

~

The interview went well. I was offered the position and started working there the following Monday. John was quite pleased that I had gone back to full-time work.

Arnie and Kitty weren't too pleased at the Crown, as I told them that John and I were leaving. Though our relationship was strained, we both decided to leave. The fun had gone from the pub as more and more houses were demolished in the slum clearance schedule. The steelworks and engineering companies were being re-located to the outskirts of the city. The off-sales at the Crown had closed down months ago. We had begun to see the changes when the police breathalyser was introduced. The customers from further afield stopped coming, or came early and left earlier, to be nearer home for their last drinks.

'Is it because of this new man in your life, Jackie?' Kitty whispered, taking me to one side.

'What new man?' I replied, too quickly.

'Come on, Jackie, you've been seen, and you need to come clean about it. It's not fair to John.'

'Kitty, my personal life doesn't concern you. Accept the fact we are leaving, and we no longer want to take over the pub. The pub's best years have gone by. I'm sorry, but that's how it is.'

'My, you've changed, Jackie. What's happened to the girl who came to us and put a smile on everyone's faces?'

I looked at the sadness in her eyes.

'She grew up, Kitty.' I gave her a hug. 'Perhaps it's time you fully retired.'

I was sorry to leave the Crown; so was John. It was a sad discussion; we both agreed in view of the circumstances, it was for the best. We'd had many happy times there and we loved the life, but things change and it was time to move on.

~

Now I was starting anew. The office I worked in was a communal one, situated over the supply depot, with various levels of employees, male and female. There were managers, typists, general clerks and the mail section. A few small private offices were along one side. My area was in the bottom corner.

I was soon made welcome by the other staff and noticed that most of the girls were younger than me. I was as old as some of their mothers, which was quite a realization. I soon forgot about the age difference, as they noticed my make-up and clothes and wanted to know where I bought them from.

'Leeds! Manchester!' they chorused when I told them.

'My mother doesn't wear clothes like you, Jackie, she's so old fashioned.' Susan Metcalf, commented, which made me feel less ancient.

The days passed quickly. Dave met me most lunchtimes and John took me home when I'd finished at five.

~

The pregnancy turned out to be a false alarm, much to my relief. I soon realised I was faster than most with my typing and working out the pricing structures. My boss was pleased and I was given a pay rise after three months.

I loved my job and working for Globe and Simpson. It seemed that life couldn't get any better as six months later; I received another pay rise and a promotion. When my quota of tasks was finished, I was moved into other areas, even the private offices if there were staff shortages. Even though I hadn't learned shorthand, I was good with audio typing, owing to my previous experience in the wholesale chemist's order department.

However, life with John was becoming unbearable. It was understandable. He knew I was still seeing Dave, who now lived in a flat on the same estate as us.

I had to have it out with him. One evening after tea in late November, I took a deep breath.

'John, I can't live like this anymore. I'm being honest with you. I love you, I always have and always will, and I also love Dave.' I fiddled with my bitten finger nails as I spoke.

John put the newspaper down.

'I'm sorry, I can't explain it any better. I remember as a child, when I was five and Jo was born. I asked Mum if she would stop loving me now we had Jo. *'Of course not, my heart's big enough for both of you,'* she said.'

I started crying as I gazed at him.

'John, look at me. Do you want me to leave?'

'No.' His voice showed no emotion. I began to sob even more and then John broke down and wept and wept, covering his head with his arms, ashamed.

I couldn't console him. I had broken his heart and I wished with all my heart that I was dead.

I went into the kitchen and made cups of tea. I couldn't hurt the man any more. I placed the tea beside his chair, and knelt by his feet.

'John. I'll finish with Dave, but let me do it my way.' He looked down at me, his eyes red and swollen. 'Let me go away with him and I'll finish it there.'

He didn't answer. The silence was only broken with gasps of air between his sobs.

'Jack, where have I failed?' he said, wiping his eyes with his hankie.

'You haven't, John, that's just it, you haven't.' I cuddled his legs. 'It's with me where the problem lies, and I can't even pinpoint what it is I want. Yet I know what I don't want,' I added.

We were both silent for what seemed like forever.

'I can't stop you from doing anything. Go and live with him if that's what you want.'

'It isn't what I want, John. I don't want to leave you.' I looked up at him and stroked his knee.

'Jack, you said you couldn't live like this.' He stood up. 'Well I can't either.'

I couldn't take any more. I ran out of the flat and down the steps, tears streaming down my face. Barging into the phone box, I phoned Dave. I waited in the basement and then the lift doors opened and John stepped out, just as Dave came through the outer doorway.

No one moved or spoke. We all just looked at each other.

Then a little woman wearing brown bootees with zipped fronts, a thick woollen coat and a headscarf fastened so tight it made her head look out of proportion to the rest of her body, came through the doorway, gasping for breath.

She stopped to catch her breath, then stared when she saw the three of us standing in silence. Dave was nearest to her. She looked him up and down and then she strained her turkey neck to look at his face.

'Ey, aren't you the plumber?' Her breathing returned to normal. 'My plughole's still blocked.'

The atmosphere was full of hostility and anger, but I suddenly wanted to laugh.

'It's not me you want, then, it's a doctor,' said Dave, straight-faced, never taking his eyes from me.

'Well, are you going to fix it or what?'

'If there's a docket in the depot for it, then someone will fix it.' His eyes were still fixed on me.

'Well, I'll hold my rent back then, and then something might get done.'

'You can hold the North Sea back for all I care, love,' was Dave's quick reply.

I'd never known him be like that with anyone and not to laugh at his quips. He turned and left.

The woman looked at me and then at John as she moved towards the lift.

'Well, I never,' she said, as the doors opened.

I turned and looked at the empty doorway, then looked back at John. He'd gone too.

I sat on the steps, crying. *I've ruined so many lives*, I thought. Great sobs rumbled through my body again as I gasped for breath. I had never known such sorrow since Shep died.

I cried again as I realised how much I missed her. The comforting long walks I took with her when there had been rows at home. She always knew when I was sad. She would place her head on my knee and look up with her trusting brown eyes. The times I cried while listening to Elvis singing 'Old Shep', and when Buddy Holly and Ritchie Valens died in that awful plane crash.

I looked up at the tons and tons of concrete above my head and leaned against the railings and peered up towards the top of the block. It was a repeating pattern of fifteen oblong shapes, getting smaller and smaller with each level. The wind howled around the block and roared down the lift shaft and rubbish chute. I wrapped my arms around my knees. A couple came in.

'Hello love, are you alright?' said the woman when she saw me. The man looked away, embarrassed, and pressed the button for the lift.

'Yes, I'm okay, thanks. I've just had a bit of bad news,' I slavered as I spoke and wiped my mouth on the back of my hand.

The woman patted my shoulder.

'Whatever it is, love, you'll not make it any easier sitting down here in the cold; you'll catch your death.'

The lift doors opened. She let go of my shoulder and followed the man into the lift. I remained on the steps until my backside turned numb with the coldness seeping through the concrete.

I stood up, wondering what to do next. Dave came back into the basement.

'Come on,' he said. 'Let's get you warmed up.' He took me in his arms.

Chapter 18

Dave's flat was cold and sparse. It was totally lacking any artistry or feminine touches. I knew I could do so much with it, but I didn't have the heart. As much as I loved being with Dave, my thoughts were never far from John.

Knowing how John always appreciated his food, I cooked, even though he was fussy about what he ate. I felt guilty cooking for someone else and couldn't help wondering how John was coping.

Needing clean clothes, I phoned Globe and Simpson, and said I wasn't coming in today as I had sickness and diarrhoea, which wasn't exactly a lie, as I did feel ill. I had a headache and my chest was tight.

Dave didn't have a washing machine in his flat, so he drove me over to the block where John and I lived with a bag of washing, during the day, when I knew John would be at work.

'See you later,' he said as he left. I pressed the lift call button and waited. I suddenly wondered if John had changed the locks as I felt in my pocket for the key. The lift doors opened and I stepped inside with my bundle of washing.

The lock hadn't been changed. I went into the kitchen and pulled the washing machine from under the worktop and pushed it over towards the sink, connected the hose to the taps and turned them on.

While the washing was in motion, I looked in the fridge. Two rashers of bacon, three eggs, a piece of mouldy cheese, a packet of lard and one of margarine plus half a bottle of milk. The pedal-bin contained an empty tin of beans and in the grill-pan, toast crumbs.

I sat down and began to cry. This was my home. As beautiful as the flat was, it was empty of love, happiness and warmth. I had ruined it all. Our wedding photo still stood on the G plan sideboard. The room divider John had made held ornaments collected on our travels. My tears fell. After a while, I stood up and went back into the kitchen to make a cup of tea.

My headache was getting worse. Opening the bathroom cabinet, I took two Panadol tablets, swallowed them dry and went into the bedroom. The cover was pulled up and over the pillow, my side of the bed untouched.

I opened John's wardrobe door. His clothes hung neatly on hangers, shirts which I had ironed with love and care. I placed my arms around them and hugged them to my chest. The tears streamed again.

The washer shuddered to a stop. Raising the lid, I removed the rubber ring and placed the clean washing in the spin dryer, refilled the tub with water, added the sheets and went back to the bedroom to get some of my clothes. I placed them on the bed and took the shopping bag from the hall cupboard, locked the door and walked down to the shops. When I returned, I placed food in the fridge, spun the other washing and pushed the machine back under the work top.

Dave came in as I was folding the damp clothes.

'Are you alright?' he asked, as he helped me to fold the sheets.

'I feel awful. I think I need some antibiotics.'

'Do you want me to get some from the doctors?'

'No thanks, it might not be much. I shouldn't get bronchitis so bad now with stopping smoking.'

We placed the clean washing in the laundry bag, collected my clothes and left.

~

We had booked tickets at the Fiesta Nightclub to see Lovelace Watkins that same night. Even though I felt and looked terrible, I made the effort and went.

We managed to park in the adjoining lay-by and were shown to our table by a young woman dressed in a costume similar to a

Playboy Bunny. Her long legs were covered in black fishnet tights and she was wearing high platform shoes, giving her a height of about five-foot ten. She took our order for drinks as we sat at the small table, one of hundreds, fixed on different levels around the sloping auditorium. Everyone had a view of the stage and dance floor. The small tables held heavy glass ash trays and small, dimly-lit lamps; the subdued glow giving everyone a glamorous and youthful appearance.

The waitress arrived with our drinks. They were expensive and as I looked around the room, I could see women taking miniature bottles from their handbags and topping up their glasses.

A Geordie warm-up comedian was struggling to entertain the Sheffield spectators.

'I was sixteen years old before I realised I wasn't a dog,' he said to the silent crowd.

He looked around and then at a woman sitting near the front. 'Are you all deaf, or what? Are you listening, pet? I said, I was sixteen before I found out I wasn't a dog – pet.' His noticeable Geordie accent rang around the room. A few titters could be heard.

Struggling, he looked at the woman again.

'Hello! Can you hear me, pet?' He turned towards the audience. 'Ah, well. Lights are on but there's no one in.'

The waitress returned with two portions of chicken in a basket. I couldn't eat mine. I was feeling worse and wanted to leave. I enjoyed watching Lovelace Watkins though; his voice made my skin tingle.

When we arrived back at Dave's flat, I went straight to bed with a hot water bottle and some more Panadol tablets.

By the following morning, I was worse and Dave took me to see the doctor, who told me I had a severe chest infection and I had to go straight back to bed. He prescribed Terramycin antibiotics and strong cough medicine and said to ring him if I was no better in two days. He also wrote me a sick note for two weeks.

After two days, there was no improvement. My lungs felt like sodden sponges; I could hardly breathe. My chest was full of gunge which wouldn't move and I was full of nausea and couldn't eat. Dave was worried and so was I. The antibiotics weren't working and by teatime, I was fearful of the coming night. I looked in the mirror; my face was grey.

'You're going to have to call the doctor, Dave.' I could hardly speak. Then I suddenly realised that my address hadn't been changed, and moreover, that I wanted my own bed and John.

~

John gasped when he saw me.

'For God's sake, what's happened?' he said as he helped me through the doorway. Dave was with me, it didn't seem to matter.

'She's got a bad chest infection,' said Dave, as John took me in his arms.

'She's got more than that,' John replied. 'Put the kettle on for a water bottle while I get her to bed.'

'The doctor's coming, John,' I said, as he took a nightie out of my drawer. He helped me to undress and get into bed.

'Listen to that wheeze,' said John, as Dave came into the bedroom with the hot water bottle. 'Why didn't you let me know?'

I wasn't looking, my eyes were closed, yet I knew how angry John was, for more reasons than one. I didn't hear Dave leave and only opened my eyes when the doctor arrived. It was a locum. He listened to my chest and back and confirmed it was bronchitis.

'But, doctor,' I managed to say. 'How can I have it this bad, I've stopped smoking?'

'Perhaps so – stopping smoking doesn't repair the damage that has already taken place. It just helps to prevent further deterioration of the lungs.' He put the stethoscope back in his bag, sighed and wrote a prescription for Aureomycin tablets. 'Take these as well as the tetracycline and finish both courses. I'm also giving you some Ephedrine and an inhalant, which should help your breathing.' He passed the prescription to John. 'Can you get these tonight? She needs to be on them straight away.'

'Yes,' John replied. 'Ferries chemist's is open until seven.'

'Good, someone will call round tomorrow. Most likely, it'll be your usual doctor. Meanwhile, stay put.' He looked at me and smiled. I closed my eyes.

Chapter 19

It was a month before I returned to work, a week before Christmas. Within two days, I was back on form. The girls told me about their problems and how some of the departments had been struggling without me. I began to feel quite important.

The following morning when I arrived, it was freezing cold throughout the building. The staff members who had already arrived were still their wearing coats and hats.

'The boiler's not working,' said Mr Ford, one of the bosses. 'They're on with it now.'

'Do you know how long it's likely to be?' I asked, shivering. People were gathered together in the general office, their arms wrapped around their bodies. 'Has any other form of heating been arranged?'

'They've gone to get some free-standing radiators,' said Alan from accounts, huddled with the rest of us.

'Well they won't warm a room the size of this,' said Pat Edwards, who handled the post.

'We'll just have to leave if it's too cold to work,' I said.

'We can't do that.' Some of the others jumped up.

'Why not? If it's too cold to work, then what are you going to do, sit here and freeze?'

'We'll just have to manage,' said Mr Ford, looking around at his staff, hoping they wouldn't walk out.

'Have you ever tried typing with gloves on?' I mumbled.

As more staff entered the premises, the situation grew worse. Everyone moaned and complained.

'Well, I'm not complaining,' I said, sitting down at my desk. 'If there's no heating on by ten o'clock, then I'm leaving. I've just recovered from bronchitis and I don't want it again.'

I looked at the work that had been placed on my desk.

Ben Ellis arrived, rubbed his hands together and grabbed his crotch. 'My, it's enough to freeze the balls off a brass monkey,' he sniggered.

'You always say that,' said Mary Peat. 'It's so you can have a crafty feel at yer balls.' She laughed and lit a cigarette. Mary was older than the other girls and quite worldly, always ready to give a quick retort to the men. She valued her job as much as her family and wouldn't hear a word against her wage paying company.

Ben Ellis moved towards her. 'Here, let's warm this up with that.' He laughed and pulled Mary's hand and cigarette towards his fly.

'Gerroff, you cheeky bugger. Wouldn't go near your crotch with a barge pole,' she said as she pulled away. 'Don't know where it's been.'

Kath, who had a soft spot for Ben, yet wouldn't admit it and blushed when confronted, looked away, embarrassed, as Ben looked towards her, raised his eyebrows and nodded.

As all the staff arrived, they gradually drifted away to their own departments and areas.

'You'll not really walk out, will you, Jackie?' asked Pat.

'I will if no heating turns up, Pat.'

'You'll get into trouble.'

'And I'll get ill again if I don't, it's as simple as that.' I inserted a sheet of letter-headed paper, carbon and copy-paper into the typewriter.

A worried look crossed her face as she hurried away and started sorting the post, still wearing her mittens. Two men arrived, carrying electric fires, then fetched more, placed them around the room and switched them on.

'Wouldn't melt butter,' grumbled Len Sharp as he tried warming his hands and feet in front of the red bars.

I struggled until ten thirty.

'I'm going to have to go,' I said to my boss. 'I'm sorry – I can't risk another chest infection. Give me a ring when it's been fixed.'

Pat rushed towards me.

'You're not leaving, are you?'

'No, I'll come back when the heating's fixed.'

Mary Peat was listening. 'They might not take you back,' she mumbled and looked away.

'They've two choices, Mary, and whichever, they'll not take my hands off me.' I went down the steps and clocked out.

~

I had to do something. But what? Our marriage was failing, and none of us were completely happy. Stolen hours with Dave; long speechless evenings with John. How much longer could it go on?

'John, I have decided to go on holiday with Dave. I will finish with him. It's impossible here. I'll tell him the purpose for the holiday when we leave and then he'll have two weeks to get over it.'

He got up from his chair and went to the bathroom without speaking.

'John,' I shouted through the door. 'Answer me, say something.' I heard the toilet flush and the tap running. Then the door opened. I stepped out of the way. 'Well, say something then…John.'

He went across the hallway and into bedroom and opened the bedroom door.

'What is there to say? You've already decided.' He took his coat from the wardrobe.

I stood in the doorway.

'But John, you don't understand…I…'

'I understand, alright. You want to live here with me and then whenever you feel like it, you want to go to bed with another man. It's perfectly clear to me, Jack. If I was reading this in a book, I wouldn't believe it.' He slipped his arms into his coat.

'It isn't perfectly clear, you don't understand…'

'So, it's all my fault,' he laughed and came towards me.

I moved out of his way as he went back into the bathroom.

110

'Where are you going?' He combed his hair in front of the mirror.

'To the Fellbrig, are you coming?' He walked towards the door.

'What's the point, we don't talk anymore. You won't even make eye contact with me. Are you that disgusted?'

'Jack, if you want me to throw you out, or tell you to leave, I'll not give you that satisfaction. I'm not the guilty party here.'

'Perhaps if you'd shown me a bit more attention instead of watching the damn football all the time, it might not have happened.'

He shrugged his shoulders, turned and left.

I went back into the room and turned on the TV. I flicked through the channels, turned it off and put a Simon and Garfunkel L.P. on the record player and curled up on the settee.

Perhaps it was time to call it a day, I thought, as the melodic sounds of 'Bridge over Troubled Waters filled my ears. A lot of our new friends had already separated and they hadn't been married as long as John and I.

I wondered if my old friends from Owlerton and Hillsborough were still together.

~

The following day, Dave and I had our photographs taken in one of the little booths with a narrow strip of curtain. I collected two passport forms from the Post Office, filled them in and sent them off with the appropriate documents and fee. I would need my own passport, now that I was going to be travelling abroad without John.

Life carried on pretty much as it had before. Christmas was the most miserable one ever, despite Noddy Holder shouting about everybody having fun from every radio and juke-box in the country and having a massive hit with 'Merry Xmas Everybody'.

John and I visited Mum and Dad, and Jo and Brian. Ian spent it somewhere down south with a new girlfriend and Dave, with his parents and children.

During the second week in January, I received a letter, along with my returned birth certificate, from the passport office, stating that the certificate was unacceptable. They needed a full one.

'That's the only one I have,' I said in despair when I phoned them. 'We need the official one…'

I cut her off. 'What do you mean, the official one? That's official – the writing's in red, it's signed and stamped.'

'The certificate you sent is dated March 1949, yet you state that you were born in September 1944. That is the one we require – the one that was issued when your birth was registered.'

I looked at the certificate in my hand and didn't know what to say or do next. My heart was thumping in my chest.

'Hello, are you there?'

'Yes, I'm here. I'm sorry, I don't know what to do.'

'Have you been adopted?'

'No, of course I haven't,' I snapped, and then I realised. 'Hello, I'm sorry, yes, my dad adopted me when he married Mum in March 1949.'

'You will need to contact the Adopted Children's Registrar at Somerset House, and ask them to send you a copy of the original. When you receive it, forward it to us, stating your original reference number and we will proceed with your application.'

I sat down on the chair near the phone.

'But I don't understand. I'm already on my husband's passport – all the necessary information was sent when we applied for that…'

'Full information wasn't required then – the birth certificate you sent then would have been dated with your adoption date, it doesn't show where you were born.'

I looked at the documents in my hand and saw the date on my birth certificate.

'It states my birth date – I don't understand…'

'If you look below your birth date, you will see it states "Certified to have been compiled from records in the custody of the Registrar-General. Given at the General Register Office, Somerset House, London, under the seal of the said office, the 19th day of August 1949." That date must have been when you were adopted, and it doesn't state your country of birth.'

I thanked her and said goodbye, then sat down. I was shocked. What a way to find out you were adopted! I wondered how many children had found out in the same way. It didn't come as a great shock to me because I already knew; what if Mum had never told me?

~

I told Mum about it next time I went to visit. Luckily she wasn't drunk. We looked through the old straw envelope bag where she kept important papers. Jo and Ian's birth certificates were there, full ones, stating their father's name and occupation, city of birth and country – England.

When my new full birth certificate arrived from Somerset house, it only showed only a surname change and the date of issue. I asked Mum why I didn't have a full one. She told me it was because she didn't name the father. I was given Mum's maiden name.

Chapter 20

I was determined not to let my personal problems overshadow my work. As the New Year progressed, there was some unrest in the offices and the Parts Department, following the AGM. There was to be no pay rise. A union meeting had been arranged and the women in my department asked me if I would go to and speak up for them. I had never been to one before. I was happy enough with my lot, so there was no point.

'Look,' I said. 'I know nothing about unions and stuff. I've never worked in a company that had a union. Haven't you got an official or someone to speak on your behalf?'

'He's not really interested.'

'Well he should be.'

They looked at each other, their faces showing discontent.

'But Jackie, you're not afraid of talking to people like that.'

'What is there to be afraid of? They can't sack you for asking questions and wanting answers.'

'Will you do it, Mary?' asked Pat.

'Not likely. I'm not putting my job in jeopardy.' Mary, in her fifties, didn't dare risk losing her job. Her husband was an idler and wouldn't work, and her kids were still demanding of her. She needed the money, the company and friendship she found at work. Mary looked at the clock. Tea-break was almost over and we made our way back to our work stations.

'What about you, Kath? Ben Ellis might be there,' Pat asked, with a wicked grin on her face.

Kath said no, and turned away, blushing.

I looked at their sad faces and couldn't understand what they were afraid of.

I managed to get hold of one of the publications circulating the managers' offices. Another outlet was to be built in the Midlands and one in Perthshire.

The paper showed images of the previous year's retirees, depicting smiling faces and grasping handshakes. New managers were being appointed; similar photographs, but younger men. I turned over the page.

LUCAS PROFITS SOAR. The headlines were clear enough, all-be-it tucked away in the bottom corner on the back page. I decided I would go to the meeting after all. It was something new, and I was always keen to learn.

~

We assembled in the canteen at five-fifteen. The tables had been moved to one side and the chairs were placed in rows. The Personnel Officer called the meeting to order and introduced the representatives. Philip McKenzie represented Lucas, and Michael Maws was our union official, a small, dapper chap. I'd seen him a couple of times before in Globe and Simpson, talking to workers in different departments.

Seating ourselves, we listened, for what seemed like an eternity, to a lot of jargon, which none of us understood.

'I wish they'd get on with it, I'm ready for my tea,' said Pat, who was sitting next to me.

I didn't answer, although I knew John would be getting annoyed, as his tea wouldn't be on time.

'Any questions? A voice said.

Susan Metcalfe, sitting on my other side nudged me. 'Jackie, stand up.'

I stood up and my mind went blank.

'Yes, your name, please,' he asked. The secretary by his side was writing everything down.

'Er, yes.' I looked around. 'Jacqueline Creek, general office.'

'Go ahead, Jacqueline.' The man sat down and conferred quietly with the chap by his side, then went over and whispered something to Michael Maws, who whispered back and shrugged.

I was holding the Lucas publication in my hand. I took a deep breath and raised the leaflet above my head.

'In the latest Lucas newssheet, it states that Lucas's profits are soaring.' I read the figures to the group. There were gasps from many who hadn't seen the bulletin and didn't know how much profit had been made. Feeling more confident, I continued.

'If Lucas can openly brag about how much profit has been made, why can't it see fit to give us a pay rise?' I remained standing.

Michael Maws looked at me, smiled and nodded his head.

The man from Lucas told me to sit down as he stood up. He was grinning.

He looked at the people sitting alongside him, then back at me.

'Jacqueline, I take it you are unfamiliar with union procedures?' He raised his eyebrows.

'Yes, sir.' I remained seated.

'Have you been to a union meeting before?' He looked again at his followers.

I realised he was taking the piss.

'No, sir, I've never even joined a union before.'

There were a few laughs and titters from certain areas. I looked around. The people around me weren't laughing. Their faces were firmly fixed.

Someone prodded me in the back.

'Go on, Jackie, tell him.'

I stood up. 'Look, if you want to know about my life history, could you please arrange it for another time? I have a tea to cook when I get home, so would you mind answering the question?'

I sat back down to a thunderous applause.

The big man's feathers had been ruffled – slightly.

'Well, Jacqueline, if you're in such a hurry to leave, I'd better get on with it.'

'Please, if you don't mind.' I was gaining confidence with every word I spoke.

'The biggest contributors to all our livelihoods are our shareholders,' he continued. 'Without them, we wouldn't have a company and you wouldn't have a job.' He stared down at us.

I stood up. 'Just a minute…'

'Sit down, Jacqueline.'

'No sir, I need to correct something. If you didn't have a workforce, your precious shareholders wouldn't have a company to collect any profits from.' I sat back down, to another round of applause.

Chairs scraped the canteen floor.

'It's the same every time…the profits have to go to the shareholders.'

Michael Maws stood up. 'Your point has been taken, Jacqueline. Can I just explain something to Mr McKenzie – before you all decide to leave?' He raised his voice as more people began to stand.

He looked at Philip McKenzie. 'This is the first time I've met Jacqueline and was unaware that there was an issue. I will now be taking the matter up on her behalf.'

Moans and groans sounded around the canteen.

'Come on, let's go home, we're wasting our time.'

'We'll not get anything with Mawsey in control.'

More chairs scraped across the floor as people made their way to the exit. I picked up my handbag.

'Well done, Jackie – that told 'em.' People patted me on the back.

'Doesn't look as if it's got us anywhere, though, does it?'

I made my way to the door. Michael Maws suddenly took hold of my arm.

'Jackie, can I have a word?' He moved me to one side and held out his hand. 'Michael Maws, your union rep.'

I shook his hand. 'Mickey Mouse, eh.'

He laughed and pulled out a packet of cigarettes. 'Smoke?'

'No thanks, it stunts your growth.' He wasn't too pleased with my reply. At five foot six, I wasn't exceptionally tall, but I was a good three inches above him.

'What are they paying you here, Jackie?' He took a long drag on the cigarette.

'Why?'

'Whatever it is, I'll make it a lot more.' He nodded his head to be more convincing. 'I could do with a smart girl like you working for me. In fact, I think we'd make a good team.'

'No thanks, Mickey. I'm quite happy where I am.' I hitched my bag over my shoulder.

'Look, you've had quite an ordeal here this evening, and shown what you're made of. You're too good for this place.'

I laughed. 'Mickey, do you call that incident in there an ordeal?' I nodded my head towards the canteen.

Mickey looked at me.

'That's tea at Buck House compared to what's really going on in my life just now.' I turned to go to the outer door.

Someone rushed down the steps. 'Well done, Jackie. Goodnight.'

I looked back at Mickey and smiled. 'Thanks for your offer, I've too much on just now.'

He handed me his card. 'Well, at least think about it,' he said as I stepped outside.

Chapter 21

'I'm sorry for the delay,' I said as I got inside the car and closed the door. 'It took longer than I thought.'

John didn't ask how the meeting had gone. He was still surrounded by a cloud of indifference.

'Seeing as it's late, shall we call for a Chinese at the Golden Dragon?'

'Suits me.' He drove as fast as the evening traffic would allow, down West Street, and turned right towards The Moor.

'I've been offered another job.'

'Are you taking it?'

'Don't you even want to know what it is?' I snapped.

'No doubt you'll tell me.' He stopped for a red light and kept his eyes straight ahead.

I felt hurt and angry and wanted Dave. Every day was the same. I choked back the tears, trying desperately to act normal.

'It's Mickey Mouse, the union chap. He wants me to work for him.'

'Mickey Mouse,' he laughed. 'Mike Maws, I've heard of him. Bit of a womaniser.' The lights changed and he moved across the Moor and onto Arundel Gate.

'So I've heard, so I'm not going.'

He gave a sarcastic laugh.

'What's so funny?' I glared at him.

He turned and parked around the back of Matilda Street.

~

We were shown to a table where I ordered mushroom soup and chicken chop suey. John chose tomato soup and beef chop suey.

I looked around at the colourful décor: lanterns, fire-spitting dragons and cascade waterfall images in elaborate gold frames: red, green and gold the prominent colours.

We sat in silence as we ate our soup. The waiter took the soup bowls away and returned with our main courses.

I looked up at his bored young face, his jet-black hair defying gravity despite the amount of gel he had used.

'This music is beautiful – what's it called?' I gestured with my hand, waving the air around my head.

John looked at me as if a frog had jumped out of my mouth.

The young waiter smiled, bowed and then admitted he didn't know. Apologizing, he walked away.

'What was that all about?' John asked as he surrendered the chopsticks for a knife and fork. 'You can't stand Chinese music.'

Before I'd had time to reply, an elderly Chinese gentleman came over to our table. He was wearing an oversized suit that must have fitted him at some time. His scrawny neck poked from the neck of a neatly ironed shirt, his tie bearing an embossed golden dragon. He reminded me of a tortoise a friend of mine had.

He bowed and began to speak. His knowledge of the English language was excellent. John paid no attention; he continued to eat his dinner. I made out that I was listening intently to a lecture about the music of the Ming Dynasty Court, and I was beginning to wish I'd never asked.

After five minutes, he bowed a couple of times and thanked me for my interest in the Ming Dynasty, bowed again and walked away.

'So?' said John, placing his knife and fork on the empty plate.

'So, what?'

'What was all that about? You weren't a bit interested in what he was saying.'

'Perhaps not, but it was certainly better than the conversations you and I've have lately.' I put down my knife and fork.

120

The young bored waiter took away the plates and brought our desserts of battered pineapple rings in syrup.

Later, after John paid the bill, we stood up to leave and the old gentleman came over. He gave us a Chinese New Year calendar, a Golden Dragon key ring, a pen, and a ten percent voucher off our next visit. He also handed me a business card with the name of the piece of music written on the back. It was written in Chinese.

~

'See, it pays to be sociable,' I said to John as we went down the stairs.

He ignored my comment. 'I'm going to look at another car on Saturday. Are you coming?'

A hint of civility. 'Well, yes, where at?' I asked as I got in the car.

'Denis's, it's a Jag, an XK150 Sports.'

'I didn't think you liked Jags.'

'This one's different. It'll be a collector's item one day.'

Denis was an old schoolmate of John; he'd gone on to become a mechanic when he'd left. After learning his trade, he'd set up his own vehicle repair business. As he progressed, he'd moved on to rebuilding more prestigious cars, such as Daimlers, Bentleys and similar vehicles, which soon became a very profitable hobby.

~

Getting the Jag put John in a better mood. I must admit, it was a looker. High-gloss maroon paint, known officially as Imperial Maroon. Spoke-wheels, a 3.8 litre engine, a top speed of 135mph and a warning sign on the dashboard stating DO NOT OPEN WINDOWS AT SPEEDS IN EXCESS OF 120 MPH.

Wherever we went, we were stopped by the police. Not for speeding, well, we were once. The police let us go. Most of the police had never seen an XK150 and were just interested, and wanted to see beneath the bonnet and all the other things men see in cars and women don't. It purred like a giant cat. A Jaguar, for sure. I could hear it a mile away, after John had left for work and when he was on his way home.

~

'How are you getting to the airport?'

It was after breakfast one Sunday morning. I was lifting a bag of flour from the cupboard to make the Yorkshire pudding. Wondering if I'd misheard, I waited a moment and then continued. I tipped some of the flour into the basin.

He said it again. This was a shock. Dave and I were due to go away at the end of the week.

'Bus, I suppose, unless Dave wants to leave his car at the airport.' I said, without turning, and took a pinch of salt from the pot, adding it to the flour.

Taking the bottle of milk from the fridge along with two eggs, I closed the door with my hip.

'I'll take you if you want. It'll give the car a good run.'

The two eggs broke in my hand as I turned. John pulled an empty dish off the worktop to catch the slimy contents sliding through my fingers. I placed the milk on the side and rinsed my hands as he passed me the hand towel.

'What's brought this on, John?' I looked at him as I wiped my hands. Then I turned and picked the eggshells from the broken eggs.

'Nothing, I just thought it would give the car a good run, through Derbyshire. Dave's car wouldn't make it to Manchester anyhow.'

I thought of Dave's old Morris Minor and how unreliable it was, yet it got him from A to B. He couldn't afford anything better; he was paying maintenance to his wife and children. I added the eggs to the flour mixture and poured some of the milk into the basin, then added water from the tap.

It was because I had said I would finish with Dave when we went away. That was why he had suggested the lift. It couldn't be for any other reason, unless he was going to lock us both in the car and set fire to it. No, he wouldn't do that to his new toy. My thoughts were in turmoil as I took the whisk from the drawer and began to beat the mixture.

'Well, if you're sure you don't mind, I'll not say no.'

'That's settled then. What time's your flight?'

I added a drop more milk to the mixture, beat it again and left it on the side to rest.

'Eleven-thirty,' I replied, not wanting to look him in the eye.

'If we leave here about nine-thirty, that should give us plenty of time, I don't think there'll be much traffic on Saturday morning.' John replied.

Chapter 22

The holiday with Dave in Majorca was over and now I had to keep my promise to John. There would be no more walks from The Belvedere, along the beach and no more dancing the night away in Tito's. I couldn't forget how he had grabbed me in the airport, held me to him and swore he would never stop seeing me.

It was now a week since I had seen him; the longest week of my life.

I remembered the sorrow in his face as he stepped out of the car when John pulled up outside his block of flats. Neither of us could speak.

John released the lock on the boot and Dave removed his suitcase. He came to the car door; a final moment of desperation.

'Jack...' His face covered in tears, he broke into a great heaving sob.

I turned away, too choked with my own tears to answer. He was still standing there in the rain as we turned the corner towards our flat.

On Monday, I returned to work. The others admired my tan, yet noticed something was amiss. Even more so when I didn't leave the building at lunchtime, whereas I was usually running down the steps and into Dave's arms. I felt like a doll without batteries. Misery was consuming me. Giving up smoking was so easy compared to this. He was my life-force, without him I was nothing.

John became more loving and showed how he cared by suggesting places to go to and things to see. My days were long and my evenings even longer.

There were times when I glanced down from the window and I could see Dave's grey van or his car, and when either pulled into the car park below, my heart skipped a beat as I waited for the familiar quiet knock. I ran to the door and looked out of the spy hole, willing him with all my heart to appear. He didn't. Minutes seemed like hours as they passed. I'd return to the living room, only to see the car or van leaving the car park.

~

One lunch time, I'd had an awful morning at work. I was feeling very down and decided to take the afternoon off. I okayed it with my boss and left the building. I decided to walk, as it was a pleasant enough afternoon. The midsummer heat had gone and gentler warmth prevailed. I walked through the park to the shops, collecting my thoughts. I did my shopping and began my return journey.

I passed the old folks home and the windows were open. I could hear Dave's voice.

Creeping towards one of the windows, I looked in. His tan had faded and he looked ill, but he still smiled at his audience.

'Two little ducks, twenty-two.' He took another tile from the bag. 'Top-of-the-house, ninety. One and seven, seventeen.' Grey-haired men and women sat around the room with bingo boards held fast in their gnarled hands.

'Two and six, half-a-crown,' he called. 'Clickety-click, sixty-seven.'

He ducked and laughed as marker pens and biros hurtled towards him.

'Dave, you've done it again!' Someone shouted.

'You promised you wouldn't do it this time,' someone else called. Dave cowered and laughed as some of the old folk resumed their places. Others left, some grinning and some annoyed.

I smiled – Dave at his best, I wanted to run and throw myself into his arms, press my head against his chest and listen to the steady pump of his heart and soul. I moved away as tears filled my eyes. I leaned against the wall, unseen, as much as one could be, surrounded by fifteen twin-tower high-rise apartment flats, and let the tears flow.

After a few minutes, I dabbed my eyes with a tissue and made my way back up the hill.

As I crossed over the footbridge towards the main road, a familiar grey van appeared. It slowed. I ran across the road, took a short-cut across the grass, through the car park and into the basement of the block. I heard the van screech around the corner and enter the car-park. He'd seen me.

Come on, come on. My finger pressed the lift-call buttons like mad. I looked up at the stairwell. There was no way I could run up fifteen flights with my shopping bag. I pressed the lift buttons again and again and then heard the lift doors open on the ground floor above. I also heard a van's door open and slam shut.

Someone was talking on the floor above. There was no point in shouting to let the lift go, they would only hold the doors open longer.

'Remember me to Harry.'

'I will, and give my regards to Connie.'

I gave an exasperated sigh as the conversation above continued, then footsteps followed by silence. The lift bounced to a stop as it arrived in the basement. The doors opened, it was empty. I dashed inside and pressed button fourteen. Placing my bag on the floor, I leaned against the metal wall, and breathed a sigh of relief as the doors began to close.

'Jack…' An arm and a large foot appeared in the closing gap, forcing the doors back open. Dave.

He grabbed hold of me as the lift began its ascent, covering my face with kisses and holding me so tight I couldn't breathe.

It was impossible to push him away. 'Dave,' I gasped. 'Stop it, I can't breathe.' He relaxed his grip.

'Not until you promise to see me again.' He spoke softly into my hair.

I clung to him. I wanted him more than anything in the world. I could never stop seeing him. This last week had been hell. Pressing me against the lift wall, he slid his arm away and reached for the

126

control panel. His keys were still in his hand; he opened the panel and jammed the lift.

We kissed, with a frenzy of passion and insanity as we grasped each other as if these were our last moments on earth together. The ground beneath us split; we were tumbling into an abyss of smoke, fire and lava and we didn't care. We wanted each other; we needed each other. We were insatiable in our lust for each other. His hands covered my body as his lips and tongue searched my mouth. I was pressed against the wall as he raised me up and onto him. His strength overwhelmed me. My body moved towards him and my hips rode the wave of mounting passion. My body shook with a tremor as it went into spasm. I cried out as he lurched and spilled himself into me and his legs buckled. The great mystifying power of love had consumed us.

~

As our breathing returned to normal, we became aware of voices.

'Are you alright in there, love?' Someone was calling. 'I've sent for the caretaker, he shouldn't be long now.'

Another voice could be heard. 'Is it broke again?'

'Caretaker's on his way.'

'Someone's stuck in it, I hope she's okay. I could hear her banging on the wall.'

I began to laugh as I came back to earth.

'He's a good caretaker, never keeps you waiting long.'

'Aye, he lived near me and our lass on't Parson Cross.'

Dave and I grinned as we tidied ourselves up. He released the lift, which jolted to a start and stopped at the next floor, just as the caretaker arrived. The doors opened.

'Oh! It's you, is it?' said the caretaker as he glanced at Dave and then me, noting our dishevelment. He smirked.

'Going up?' said Dave as the people stepped back and the doors closed.

Chapter 23

'I'm sorry, John. I've started seeing Dave again. I know I promised.' I had to tell him; I couldn't live with my conscience. It was about a week after Dave and I had been stuck in that lift.

We had eaten our tea and he was reading the evening paper. His face and eyes darkened. He stood up, raised his arms above his head and pushed back his hair. He didn't speak, and then he turned as if to say something, then stopped and shook his head. I moved towards him.

'John…' I lowered my head. What could I say that would make things right between us? There was no turning the clock back. And the hardest part of all was that I still loved John no less – more, in fact, for putting up with me and loving me like he did.

The phone suddenly rang, shattering the silence. John answered it. I followed him into the hallway.

'It's your mother.' He handed me the phone.

I listened to her drunken ramblings and eventually put the phone down.

'It's Dad, he's poorly again, and she wants me to go down.'

John didn't hesitate. 'Are you going now? I'll take you.' He picked up the keys from the hall table, checked that there was nothing still on the cooker and made his way to the door.

My heart was so full of love for him, I wrapped my arms around his neck; he pulled away.

He opened the door for me as I stepped out, then turned and locked it. We made our way to the lift. A pang of guilt hit me as the lift doors opened and I looked at the locked control panel. He pressed the button for the basement and the lift descended.

Mum was sleeping it off in the chair when we arrived. Dad was in bed and didn't look at all well. I went over to him and took his hand.

'Dad, Dad, it's me, wake up.' His breathing was raspy. I shook him gently and looked at John. John's face looked grave. I shook him again.

'Dad, are you all right?' His eyes slowly opened and began to focus.

He realised I was holding his hand and gave it a squeeze.

'Has the doctor been, Dad?' I raised my voice, realizing his hearing had deteriorated.

I looked around the bedroom; there was no medication to be seen.

'John, have a look downstairs for me, please. See if there are any medicines knocking about. And bring me the thermometer up,' I added when he was halfway down the stairs.

I stroked Dad's hand and stroked his fevered brow.

'Can you hear me, Dad?' He didn't reply. I tucked his hand under the cover and went downstairs. Mum was snoring away in the chair.

'Can't find anything, Jack,' said John as he took the thermometer from the first aid box and handed it to me.

'We need to get her awake,' I said, nodding towards Mum. 'Make her some coffee please, while I take Dad's temperature.'

Mum was awake when I went back down, her eyes bleary and unfocused.

'What are you doing here?' she slurred.

'You called me, remember? How long has Dad been ill?'

'What's it to you?' she snapped.

'More than it is to you, obviously!' I snapped back. 'Has the doctor been?'

'He doesn't want the doctor, he says he just wants to rest.' She slurped the scalding hot coffee.

John sat in Dad's chair and began reading the newspaper, leaving us to it.

'When did he last eat? Mum?' She was dozing again. I took the cup from her and placed it on the table.

'John, I'm going to stay here tonight and get the doctor in tomorrow. I need to see him.'

'Are you sure? I'll stay with you if you want.'

'No, love, you've got to get up early for work. I'll be okay. I need to make sure she doesn't have any more to drink. Oh! And will you ring Jo for me please when you get back and tell her what's happened?'

'Isn't Ian here?'

'I don't think so, I looked in his bedroom and it doesn't look like it. He's probably working away again. Just check my purse and see if there's any change to phone the doctor in the morning and my bus fare home.'

'Do you want me to ring the doctor in the morning? It'll save you leaving the house.'

'Yes, if you don't mind. Will you phone work for me too, please?' I jotted the doctor's phone number and my work's number on a slip of paper, and handed it to him. He squeezed my hand. I wrapped my arms around him.

'Thanks, John.' I choked back the tears. 'I do love you, you know.' He held me close.

'I love you too,' he replied, giving me a hug.

~

After he'd gone, I found some orange barley water in the pantry, made Dad a hot drink and gave him two Panadol tablets. I went back downstairs and managed to move Mum over to the settee and covered her with the quilt from Ian's bed. *If he comes home tonight, it's tough*, I thought.

I went across the yard to the toilet, locked the doors when I came back, took a glass of water upstairs with me, then got into bed next to Dad.

It was eleven o'clock next morning when the doctor arrived. After giving Dad a thorough examination, he decided that Dad would be better in the hospital as he had a severe case of bronchitis. The doctor feared that because of the delay in getting him on antibiotics, pneumonia couldn't be ruled out. He added that at his time of life, his age was against him.

'He'll not go into hospital,' I said. 'It will finish him off.' I held Dad's hand; he couldn't hear what we were saying.

'I can't look after him,' said Mum when the doctor and I went downstairs. The doctor ignored her comments and wrote a prescription.

'Get him on these as soon as possible and I'll call in two days – they should be into his system by then. I'll also get a district nurse to come and take a look and see if anything can be done.' He handed me the prescription, fastened his bag and left.

'Doctor…' I called as I grabbed my bag and followed him out. 'What about Mum?'

He stopped and turned as I caught up with him in the entry.

'Can't anything be done? I know I've asked you before – you can see for yourself what she's like, she's not capable of looking after Dad. I can't do it, I work full-time.'

He shook his head.

'I'm sorry – unless she admits to herself she has a drink problem, there's nothing we can do.'

'She'll never admit to having a drink problem, doctor. Every time I tell her about it, we end up having a flaming row.' We stood by his car.

'Look, I'll get a welfare officer to call round and take it from there.' He opened the car door. 'I'm sorry I can't give you a lift to the chemist.' He glanced at the prescription in my hand. 'I've more calls in this area.' He started the car and drove out of the street.

~

My mind was in turmoil as I made my way to Middlewood Road. How would I know when the welfare inspector was coming? Surely they would send a letter first, or would they arrive unexpectedly, to catch you out if you were falsifying a claim. I didn't know, I'd never had experience of such things, yet I needed to know. I had to speak to them – it would be no good Mum talking to them. As drunk as Mum got, she would never accept help of any kind; she'd too much pride.

I decided that I would phone Jo tonight, to see if she had any suggestions.

'I'll call back in five minutes,' I said as I handed the prescription over the counter and went across to the phone box.

I dialled the depot and pressed button A when someone answered. The coins dropped.

'Hello. Can you give a message to David, please? Can you tell him Jackie's at her mum's?'

'Big Dave?'

'No, little Dave.'

'Okay, got it.'

'Thanks.' I replaced the receiver and went back to the chemist.

~

Jo said she couldn't do anything at the moment as they were in-between jobs.

'What's brought this on – you've not mentioned anything before?'

This was the problem with Jo and Brian; they could be so secretive. I was standing in the hallway, back at the flat. After half an hour, I put the phone down and went into the living room to talk to John.

'What was that about?' he asked.

'Jo can't help,' I said as I sat down on the settee. He swivelled the G plan chair around to face me. 'They're leaving the teaching profession.'

John put down the paper. 'They're what?'

'Yes, it shocked me too. They can't get a position in the same school in Sheffield, so Brian's leaving the teaching profession to manage one of the Social Security offices, and Jo's going to work as a clerk in the West Street office.'

132

'There's more to this than meets the eye,' said John, his brow furrowed.

'Well, you know how secretive they are. Come on, let's go and see how Dad is, I've got to go back to work tomorrow.'

Chapter 24

Somehow, Dad made an unexpected recovery. The doctor did explain that there could be a relapse and he didn't give much hope for next time. He said that his heart was now affected.

Dad now had to take regular medication, which wasn't easy, as he didn't want to take so many tablets and Mum was incapable of administering them. The illness had taken its toll on Dad and I feared the worst and wondered how long he had left.

Sadness overwhelmed me as I looked at Dad's crumbling body as he sat in his armchair. The news of Harold Wilson's retirement brought Dad down even further. I wondered what else could be done. There was to be no help from a day nurse, and there was no bathroom in the house, so nurses couldn't attend.

I gave him a cuddle and looked at the large blue veins rising from his hands as I held them. My tears welled up. I couldn't let him see me like this.

'Don't let them take me to the hospital, please.' He looked up at me, his faded eyes hardly seeing anything. His face showed the deep sorrow of one who had lived too long.

I choked back my tears. 'I won't, Dad. I promise.'

~

Dave was anxious about what had happened to warrant my sudden disappearance. He already knew of the problems with my family.

'And that's it?' he said, annoyed. 'They won't give him home care because there's no bathroom? I don't believe it.' He shook his head.

'It's true, Dave. The nurses can't attend unless there are bathroom facilities.'

Dave began to pace and stroked his chin.

'Well that's easily fixed,' he said, slapping his hands together. 'I'll put a bathroom in.'

I jumped up. 'Dave, you can't.'

'Who says? You own the house, don't you?' He started pacing again. 'Where's the drains?'

'What drains, what are you on about?'

'On the back, on the front?'

'Oh! They're on the back.'

'How big is the back bedroom?'

'About twelve foot by twelve, why?'

'We could put a bathroom in and make the bedroom into a smaller one. John can do the partitioning and put in another door, I'll do the plumbing, Mick'll do the wiring…'

'Hang on a minute – we can't afford it, Dave. We spend our money as fast as we earn it.'

'It'll not cost a lot. I can get a "seconds" bath, and John can get the timber. We can do it in the evenings and at the weekends.'

'Dave, it's a lovely idea and I'm very grateful – but why would you want to do such a big job? You don't even know my parents.' I shook my head. Dear Dave, he always meant well.

He came closer and took me in his arms.

'I know you.'

~

John didn't like the idea when I told him.

'John, we can't afford to do it on our own, and you'll not get any money from Jo or Ian towards the cost. Put aside our differences, John. This isn't for me, it's for Dad. And don't forget, we own the house and it can only increase its value.'

The more he thought about it, the more it grew on him and before long, he sat down and drew up a plan and a list of requirements.

We arranged to pick Dave up from work after tea one evening and go down and take a look.

Mum wanted to know what was going on, and then decided it would be better than having to go across the yard to the toilet. I'm not sure if Dad understood, but he knew he wasn't going into hospital and that was good enough for me.

The atmosphere between John and Dave was strained; John insisting that Dave hadn't a clue about anything, and that was just discussing the work plan.

'All council workers are the same,' he moaned.

'Get on with it,' I replied. 'He served his apprenticeship, the same as you. This isn't for me, it's for Dad.' I snapped, tired of the constant bickering.

~

A lot of the materials we were going to use had already been taken to Mum's and placed in the bedroom. The walls had been marked, where the fittings were going to go, and the landing wall was marked for the sledge-hammer.

Mum and Dad were in the front room: we were sitting in the kitchen having a coffee and checking our notes before we left, when Ian arrived with another girlfriend. He seemed slightly quieter than usual, which must be the effect his new girlfriend had on him. He introduced her as Lynda. She said hello, with a well-educated southern accent and sat quietly by Ian's side. Something was wrong, I could sense it.

Ian reverted to his former self and asked who the meat-loaf was, referring to Dave.

'Sorry, I thought you were a wrestler. I'll bet my mother's took to you,' he laughed.

I ignored him. He didn't stop there.

'Boyfriend, Jack?' he said, grinning. 'Oops sorry, John, didn't see you there.'

'Fuck off, Ian.' I don't know where it came from, it just came out.

'Language, Jacqueline, language.' He waved his finger at me.

'Sit down, Ian,' said John, his face ashen.

'Dave's here to put the bathroom in.'

'Bathroom? Where?' said Ian, lighting a cigarette.

'The back bedroom, why?'

Lynda jumped up.

'Ian – you...'

He cut her off. 'You can't put a bathroom in – we need the bedroom.' His face was serious.

'Too bad!' I replied. 'Dad needs a bathroom.'

'But...Well, you'll find out sooner or later. Lynda's preggers.'

Chapter 25

I had to get back to work. I was fed up with all the upset of late, settling disputes regarding the bathroom with John and Dave; the problems with Mum and Dad; Ian and his dilemma.

'I thought you'd have had more sense,' I said to Ian when I caught him on his own. 'Jo and I managed it, I'm sure you could have.'

'She told me she was on the pill.' He lit a cigarette.

I wasn't sure what to make of that. Who was I to judge? I wafted the smoke away.

'Do you really have to put a bathroom in, Jack? They've managed without one all these years.'

'Yes, we do. Dad's health is more important than your *slip-up.*'

He took another drag on the cigarette, blowing the smoke in the other direction.

'But Jack, we need to live somewhere.'

'Ian, you're twenty-three. Start facing up to your responsibilities. You can't bring a baby into this house. Dad's too old and too ill, and look at the state of Mum. It wouldn't be right to subject a baby to that anyhow. I'll say to you what Mum said to me not long after I'd been married and wanted to come back home. *You've made your bed – now lie on it.*'

~

Back at work, it felt good to be part of the team again. *Mickey Mouse* called in to see me to say we had got the pay rise and then asked if I'd had a change of heart about working for him. I thanked him once again and declined. I'd enough responsibilities already.

I began thinking about the company and my worth. I was at the lower end of the payroll. How many were above me in the ratings? I thought about the various offices and department, each with their individual staff, managers and under-managers. That was just here, in Sheffield, just one branch of many, all under the Lucas umbrella.

I knew company directors earned unbelievable salaries. John told me about the directors at Tinsley Wire, and their luxury houses in Fulwood, Dore and Derbyshire.

How did they get these positions? A good education, obviously, but how much did luck come into it, or was it through contacts already on the money ladder? And was it ever possible to get to the top with so many others on the higher rungs? I switched my thoughts to Ben Ellis.

Ben Elis was retiring and we were arranging a leaving party for him. A slip of paper with suggestion for gifts was passed around the office by sleight of hand. As soon as he was out of the room, we discussed the most appropriate gift. The monetary collection was good.

Ben was well-liked by all, male and female. He always had a cheery smile and kindly words; the joker of the office. Some of his jokes could be quite crude, yet the way he told them was never derogatory. He was innovative and informative, and would talk about things that were close to being distasteful, yet he never overstepped the line. His comments and remarks were always humorous and never suggestive.

He told us once that he had bought some anal beads for his wife's birthday, and didn't have the heart to tell her that she looked like Wilma Flintstone because she was wearing them around her neck. We laughed because he did, and then looked around at each other – *what on Earth were anal beads?*

He had sciatica in his lower back and sometimes, he would jump up from his chair in pain, rub his back, shake his head and say – 'I knew that butt-plug was too big.'

A lot of the women got a verbal sexual education from Ben, who was always willing to answer the most confidential questions in a serious manner, which must have roused some curiosity with their husbands and boyfriends.

We decided on an engraved pewter tankard and a book of jokes for the over sixties, signed by us all. I wanted to give him a personal gift and thought of making him a pouch to keep his anal beads in, and then I decided on a willy-warmer, as he was always moaning about the cold and brass monkeys. It was a joke, yet it needed to be somewhat authentic.

I drew some images to work out how it could be formed. I found an off-cut of red fur fabric on the market, cut out a basic shape and stitched it together on Mum's sewing machine, which I had claimed. I lifted it from the machine. It was looking good, with an opening for the contents, and it now needed a closure. Threading a length of narrow black ribbon through the casing at the top, I drew the ribbons tight and tied them in a bow. Having formed a basic pattern, I wasn't too sure of the measurements and couldn't ask Ben Ellis, although he probably would have enjoyed the banter. So I asked John if he would oblige, which turned out to be an impossible task!

'You've always had nice legs, John, a true biker's legs,' I said, unfastening the bow and trying in vain to get him into it.

'Keep still, John. I'm trying to fasten it.' We were in the living room at the flat. He was standing in front of me with his trousers and underpants around his ankles.

'How can I keep still when you're knelt in front of me fiddling with my willy?' he said, his erection growing, as my hand tested the fit.

I fastened the narrow ribbon on top and slipped a finger beneath.

'Is it too tight?'

His hips started convulsing.

'Give over, John. This is serious. I want it to be right.' I looked up at him. His head lolled to one side, eyes glazed, staring out the window.

It would have to do; it was near enough, I decided. After cutting out another, I sewed it together and wrapped it in tissue and gift wrapping paper.

Chapter 26

Work began on the bathroom for Dad. The bedroom's fireplace was removed and pipes were laid. Another doorway was knocked in the landing wall for the smaller bedroom, along with openings for the bathroom window and pipe work in the outer wall.

There wasn't much I could help with in Dave's area, so I fastened the room separation plaster boards to the timber framework John had placed in position, while he cut and sawed lengths of wood for the new window frame and doorway.

Mum, having one of her sober-ish evenings, came up with teas and coffees.

'Mrs Yates's house next door is coming up for sale,' she said, as she looked for somewhere to place the mugs.

John moved a piece of timber from the trestle to make space.

'Who's selling it?' I asked, helping myself to a sawdust-covered biscuit.

'Mr Simpson, the landlord. They rented it until Vic died and then Ethel went into an old people's home.'

'Is old Simpson still alive?' I blew the dust off the biscuit and dipped it in the tea.

'As far as I know, he is – his son's took over now though.'

'What's that?' asked Dave, wiping his hands on a piece of old towel.

'Our old landlord, ask Dad about him. No don't, don't want to give him a heart attack.' I looked back at Mum and dunked another biscuit. 'How much is he asking?'

'I don't know,' she replied, looking around. 'Oo! It's a big job.' She moved towards the window.

'Mind where you tread, don't want you getting a nail in your slipper,' said Dave as he finished his coffee and handed her the empty mug.

'Have you got his phone number?' I asked as I handed her my mug.

'I'll find it for you before you leave,' she said and took the mugs and plate downstairs.

'What are you thinking of?' asked John as he placed the new door frame in position.

'Nothing – I'll tell you tomorrow.' I picked up a handful of clout nails and continued hammering them into the plaster boards.

There was the usual uneasy silence as John drove us home when we'd finished. We pulled up outside the chip shop and bought fish and chips to take away. Dave said he'd walk the rest of the way as it wasn't far.

'It's Ben Ellis's leaving do on Friday. Don't forget we'll be going for a drink straight from work,' I said to John as he got back in the car with our supper.

I was on the phone before I went to work the following morning.

'Hello, is that Mr Simpson?'

'Yes, who's calling?'

'Charlie Campbell's daughter, Jacqueline. I used to live on Tanfield Road – my husband and I bought Mum and Dad's house from you.'

'That'll have been my dad, he's retired now. I'm Graham, his son. How can I help?'

'I hear next door's for sale, number twenty-six. How much do you want for it?'

~

The pub was full with early evening drinkers, passing time until the rush hour traffic cleared. Eight of us had put a pound each into the kitty to pay for the drinks. As it was Ben Ellis's leaving-do, he had to buy the first round. Betty, the landlady had reserved a couple of tables for us. Making our way through the smoky atmosphere to the bar, we placed our order.

'I'll bring the sandwiches over in a minute, love,' Betty said, as she poured an extra splash of blackcurrant juice into Mary's glass of lager. She stamped her foot loudly on the wooden trapdoor. 'Sam.' She bent over to lift the hatch. 'Sam, the lager's gone now,' she called and banged the door shut.

Ben Ellis came in and made his way towards us, to a loud cheer.

'Blimey! What are you all supping – Champagne?' he said, as he paid for the round of drinks. 'It's a good job I'm not taking you lot out often. Twenty-one pounds fifty a week pension wouldn't go far.'

'Twenty-one pounds fifty, I wish I was getting that for a wage,' said Donna Richards.

He looked at her as he picked his pint up from the bar.

'Ey, that penison's for two of us, mind!'

'Cheers! Ben, we hope you have a long and happy retirement.' We raised our glasses and eased our way to the reserved tables.

Sitting down, Ben rubbed his hands together. 'Come on then, what have you got for me then? Don't keep me in suspense.' He took the top off his pint of Guinness and licked the thick foam from his top lip.

The music from the juke-box became louder as the crowd began to disperse.

'Money, Money, Money,' we all sang in unison as the voices of Abba could now be heard. We shouted the lyrics about wanting a wealthy man and leaned in towards Ben Ellis. Donna sat on his knee and stroked his chest while singing to him.

'Don't stop there, Donna.' Ben tried to unfasten his front shirt buttons.

Betty interrupted the sing-along by placing two large plates of sandwiches on the tables. Her daughter Eileen helped by carrying a large pork pie, cut into wedges, a bottle of Henderson's Relish and a jar of pickled onions.

'Money, Money, Money,' she sang to Ben, then turned and made her way back to the bar for some serviettes.

We ate sandwiches and gave Ben his gift – an engraved Wentworth Pewter tankard in a royal blue, satin-lined box. He dabbed his eyes with his handkerchief as he read the inscription and the card, signed by almost everyone who worked for Globe and Simpson.

'Let's get some more drinks, Kitty's paying,' said Pat as she stubbed her cigarette end into the ashtray and stood up. 'Have you got it?' she whispered as we made our way to the bar.

'Yes.' I nodded.

'Jackie's got something else for you,' said Pat when we returned.

He looked up, and the girls went quiet. None of them knew what I had made, although they knew I had a surprise for him. I reached under the seat for my handbag. The girls were just as excited as Ben as I removed the gift-wrapped present and handed it to him.

Some of the regulars noticed the sudden silence and looked on, as Ben Ellis slowly unwrapped the furry gift. Standing up, he carefully opened the folded tissue paper and lifted the gift for all to see.

His eyes widened. 'It's a willy-warmer.'

The customers erupted into laughter. Kath choked on her drink as she saw what he was holding, and then blushed.

'Did you make it?' asked Sandra, turning to look at me.

'Jackie, it's fantastic, will you make me one?'

'Can I have one?'

'I want one too.'

I was besieged by people wanting them.

Ben Ellis's face was a picture. 'I wish I'd brought a camera,' said Joan.

'Go on then, Ben, try it on…' Kath blushed again at her own juvenile remark. Ben was just as surprised.

'Go on Ben, try it on,' said Donna, taking hold of his hand and pulling him up from the seat.

144

'Go on, Ben – On. On. On,' we chanted.

Not having much option, Ben stood up. 'I can tell you now,' he said, looking at us as we became louder. 'It's much too small.'

We pushed him towards the Gents toilet. 'On. On. On.'

'Do you do them in men's sizes?' laughed Sam behind the bar as he wiped a pint pot and placed it on the shelf.

'Yes, he would definitely need a smaller one,' quipped Betty as she poured a Cherry B into a stem glass.

The crowd standing by the bar looked at Sam and laughed.

'Ahh, secret's coming out now, eh Sam?'

Ben came out of the toilet, his fly slightly open and the willy-warmer hanging out.

'Da dat da da, da dat da da…' We began singing the stripper tune as he walked from the toilet, hands on his swaying hips. The other drinkers clapped to the tune. So did Betty and Sam. He sashayed over to Mary, who, finding no escape, went quiet and backed into her seat.

'What do you think, Mary? Does it fit?'

Kath looked on, embarrassed and envious.

He stood before her, shaking his pelvis. Mary didn't know what to say or do, but her eyes were smiling.

Donna suddenly grabbed hold of it and pulled it free from his fly.

'Thought as much,' she said, holding it in the air with the toilet paper he had used to fill it. 'Miles too big.'

The men by the bar booed and laughed, while Ben, not trusting Donna, quickly zipped his fly.

Another round of drinks was bought by "Kitty" and more sandwiches were eaten. Bryan Ferry's voice came from the juke-box and we sat around the tables, holding hands and singing 'Let's stick together' to Ben.

The early drinkers gradually left to make their way home; we continued to give Ben a good send-off.

Donna reached towards the table, picked up a spoon and took a pickled onion from the jar. Holding it between her front teeth, she turned towards Ben, indicating with her fingers for him to take the onion by using only his teeth. She bounced around in front of him while moving to the music. Ben Ellis reached in his pocket for his handkerchief, held it to his mouth and dropped his false teeth into it.

Donna jumped up, spat the onion out of her mouth and screamed. Ben peeled the handkerchief back and rushed towards her, clacking the teeth in his hand while making gurning motions with his mouth.

'Gerr-away!' She pushed him away as she tried to escape, but we shoved her back towards him.

'Go on Ben, she's all yours,' we said, as more tears smudged our mascara.

Mary suddenly stopped laughing: a look of horror crossed her face as she stood up, then burst out laughing again as she dashed past us.

'I've gone and peed my pants now.'

As the evening wore on and the later drinkers arrived, we knew it was time to call it a day. Not all the women were single or had grown-up children, so it was only fair that we all left together.

As we made our way to the door, we hugged, and with tear-filled eyes, kissed Ben Ellis farewell. The office wouldn't be the same without him. He'd be missed. Kath's fondness for Ben showed as she wept openly. Ben held her close, stroking and patting her back.

'I'll keep calling in to see you. You'll not get rid of me that easily,' he said, looking into her sad eyes.

'Don't forget, we want a photo of you wearing the willy-warmer,' said Donna as she lit a cigarette and made her way to the bus stop.

My journey was in the other direction.

'I'll see you on Monday.' I turned and made my way to the crossing.

'Don't forget the willy-warmers,' they called as I stepped onto the road. I had taken orders for twelve and wondered how I would find time to make them.

Chapter 27

The following morning, I was up the ladder, pointing the bricks around the new window Dave had put in. Dave was plastering the boards inside and John had gone to the builders' merchants. I looked down as I heard a voice.

'Very impressive. Do you want a job?'

'No thanks, I've already got one.' A young man around my age was staring up at me.

'You must be Charlie's daughter,' he said, as I came down the ladder and placed the trowel and mortar board on the windowsill.

I wiped my hands on my old jeans as he offered his hand.

'Graham Simpson – we spoke on the phone.'

'Sorry,' I said as I shook it.

'Don't apologise, I'm the same during the week. You don't have nice hands in the building trade. Mind if I look around?' He glanced towards the doorway.

'No, not at all,' I said, leading him into the house and up the stairs.

He followed me into the new bathroom, his eyes looking everywhere.

'So who's the builder?'

'This is my friend Dave, he's a plumber.'

He nodded to Dave, who was mixing another bucketful of Carlite Thistle plaster.

'My husband John is a joiner – he's just gone to the builders' yard.'

He looked at me. 'Do you work with them full time?'

'Me! No, we've all got full-time work. We're only doing this so Dad doesn't have to go in hospital.'

'So what's the interest in next door?' He nodded goodbye to Dave and made his way to the top of the stairs.

I followed him down.

'We've almost finished this one – thought we might buy the other one and modernize it, depending on what price you're asking.'

He made his way to the door.

'Not going to live in it, then?'

'Not likely,' I laughed. 'Next door to my mother, you must be joking. Someone else can have that pleasure.'

We stood in the doorway. He took out a business card and handed it to me.

'I would be advertising it at £1,225.' He searched my face, waiting for a response.

'That counts us out then – thanks for your time.'

'Hold on a minute, what figure did you have in mind?'

'Nothing like that figure, I thought less than a thousand.'

He laughed. 'Property prices are rising all the time, big demand for houses in this area.'

'We didn't pay anything like that when we bought Mum and Dad's.'

'That was a long time ago – they've gone up a lot since.'

'Maybe for some – and next door's not been touched for years. It would need gutting.'

'Indeed, but what would it be worth modernized, eh?' He stressed the point.

'Five-thou!' I replied.

'Well, you've done your homework.'

'I'm not just a pretty face, you know.'

I heard Dave coming downstairs. 'Is that kettle on?' he called.

My eyes followed his every move as he made his way to the sink. How could any man washing a bucket look sexy? He must have felt my eyes on him and glanced over. My lip twitched at the corner as he raised his eyes to the upstairs and nodded. The grin began to spread across my face as I looked back at Graham.

'I'll be off then, you'd better make your *friend* a drink.' He winked and looked over at Dave, now drying his hands.

'Would you take a thousand?' I said as he rose to leave. 'It's not mortgageable,' I added.

He stepped outside. 'I never said it was.'

'So how do you expect to sell it?'

He laughed again. 'I'll have a word with my Dad, and tell your *friend* Dave, if he ever needs a job to give me a call, we're always on the lookout for good workers.'

John came back just after Graham Simpson left.

'There's some tea in the pot, John, do you want some?'

'Please, who was that?' He placed tins of paint and primer on the kitchen table.

'Landlord – Simpson's son. Tried to do a deal with him for next door but he wouldn't have it.'

We sat drinking tea. Dave joined us.

'How much does he want for it?' asked Dave, taking a gulp of scalding hot tea.

'How can you drink tea as hot as that? It can't do your stomach any good.'

John looked away and made no comment.

'He's asking £1,225 for it,' I continued.

'He'll get it – a smaller builder will buy it at that price,' John said, while reading the wording on the primer. 'It needs a lot of work doing on it.'

'Yes, if we put a bathroom in like we've done here and add a dormer window in the attic, you've got a three-bedroom house.'

'Jack,' sighed John. 'You're missing something important here. Where's the money coming from to buy next door?'

'The bank, won't they loan it us?'

'Of course not, the house isn't mortgageable.'

'It will be. Don't be so dismissive.' I put down my cup and stood up.

'There's got to be a way. I'll make an appointment to see them.'

John sighed again and drank his tea. Dave listened, unspeaking.

'I'll just say ta-ra to Dad before I go. I've to call in the market on the way home for some fur fabric and cord.'

Dad came in from the front-room.

'I thought you'd gone, with it going quiet.'

'What? We wouldn't go without saying ta-ra. Sit down, I'll get you a coffee.' I stroked his head as he sat at the table.

~

I made the willy-warmers over the weekend and took them into work on Monday morning. At tea-break, some were passed around to each department, and as more people saw them, more people wanted them – and in different colours. Before the day was over, I had taken orders for twenty-seven. The following day, more orders came in and then again the following day and every day until the weekend.

On Saturday morning, John went down to the market for some more fur fabric, while I changed the bedding and did the washing. Dave went down to Mum and Dad's to do more work on the house. John joined him, after setting me up with a piece of eight-by-four, which he placed on top of the dining room table. It was very hard work, cutting the willy-warmers out on the floor and the block-board made a big difference to the strain on my back.

The weekend passed too quickly. Many household tasks remained unfulfilled and I had only sewn a few of the willy-warmers. Cutting them out had taken longer than I thought. Because of the thickness of the fabric, only one layer could be cut at a time. I had to come up with something. Meanwhile, I had to get to the bank to see about a loan.

~

'What do you mean, we've no collateral? We've been with you all these years and got our word on it. All our car HP payments have been paid on time, our rent and electricity – everything is paid on time.'

'Look, Mrs Creek, you need a mortgage to buy a house. Why don't you come back with your husband and let's hear what he has to say?'

He stood up. His shiny black suit was a size too small – no wonder he needed to stand up.

I remained seated.

'We don't want a mortgage, we want to buy the house, renovate it and sell it. What's the problem? Isn't our word good enough? Just because we're council tenants doesn't mean our money's not as good as someone with their own house.'

'I've only got *your* word, and I want to know what your husband thinks.'

'He's at work and I can speak on his behalf. He'll not take time out, he has a responsible position. He'll come down and sign when the paperwork is done.'

'Look, Mrs Creek, there isn't going to be any paperwork…'

I jumped up.

'How come we can buy a car and drive it away by paying a deposit and a promise to pay the instalments? What's the difference?'

He brushed back the front of his hair and adjusted his tie. 'You're not listening to me…'

'Oh yes I am, and I know there are such things as home improvement loans available from the banks. You're just refusing us because we're council tenants.'

'Home improvement loans are for people who already have a home.' He sighed, placed his fists on the desk and shook his head.

'And how are we supposed to get a home if you won't lend us the money?' I snapped and picked up my handbag. 'There's more flaming banks than the Midland. I'll go elsewhere,' I shouted.

I slammed the door as I left. Then realised it was a swing door.

~

I was struggling and having to take time off work to make the willy-warmers. Mum's old sewing machine had had its day, so I needed to buy another one, which was nowhere near as good as Mum's old Singer. John had taken some willy-warmers to work and he too was taking orders on them. Our second bedroom in the flat was crammed with red, black, pale blue and royal blue fur fabric, along with boxes of cord, ribbons and sewing threads. We had decided to stock pile some willy-warmers over the winter, then take them to the seaside next spring. The trouble with this was that we would be paying out money for materials and wages, whilst the monetary returns would not be coming in.

I had placed an advertisement in the local post office to see if I could find a home-worker. It didn't last long; the women were forever moaning about the fur fabric fluff being all over the house. Well, what did they expect? If it wasn't that, it was the fact that their machines were burning out and they wanted me to replace them. They weren't satisfied with the work being delivered and collected promptly and being paid a fair rate to cover electricity costs too.

Eventually, I found another woman who had an excellent machine. It was an industrial Pffaf. She was called Ellen Toulson, and she told me that she used to work for S.R. Gent's on piece work, but as she aged, piece work became too much for her, so now she worked from home, taking in work whenever she could get it. I told her that if she did a good job, I could probably give her regular work.

I couldn't believe my eyes when I saw how fast she was. She could see the look of amazement on my face.

'It'll run twenty-four hours a day non-stop if needs be.'

I was mesmerized, watching how her hands fed work to the needle. Hands and feet in perfect co-ordination – years of factory work had given her this skill.

'Can I have a go?'

'I wondered when you'd ask.' She glanced up at me, laughed and finished the sample, then raised her feet from the treadle and switched it off. We changed places. 'Just remember one thing – the machine will always be faster than you.'

She switched it back on. The room slowly filled with a constant low whine. 'Lift the fabric presser foot up with your knee.'

'My knee? Don't I do it by hand?'

'No, you hold the fabric with both hands and place it under the foot.' She was watching me closely. 'That's it, you're doing great. Now release the foot – with your knee, that's it, the foot's got the fabric.'

The heavy motor keened and hummed beneath the bench, and I realised this must be the precision engineering Len used to talk about.

'My, Jackie, you're quick on the uptake. I can see you going places. Now ease your feet slowly up off the treadle, that's it, take it steady – this machine can punch the needle through your fingers before you've screamed.'

We both laughed. I felt the power beneath my feet and hands. A thrill ran through me, and this time I wasn't thinking of Dave.

I told John about the industrial machine later when we were in bed. He said it was the same with cars – how high-powered cars differed from the regular ones.

'If that's so, I want to learn to drive.'

'If that's why you want to learn, then you're learning for the wrong reasons. Don't ask me to teach you.' He turned over and switched off the light.

I lay thinking. My mind was on fire. So many things were happening and I loved it. I turned over and put my arm around John. Poor John, he loved me so much and I was wicked. I didn't deserve him. Our lovemaking had ceased. I snuggled my head to his back and stroked his arm. My sobs came quietly.

~

I awoke next morning knowing I had to leave work. Even though John had made me a couple of hardboard templates for cutting the willy-warmers, it was still taking a long time, even with both of us working either side of the table. The money I was collecting was almost as much as my wages. I told Dave I was leaving work; he was thrilled.

'What's happening about the house next door to your mother's? I didn't like asking while John was present – I think it's a good idea too.'

'We can't get the money, Dave. The bank won't cough up.'

153

'I didn't like saying while John was there, but if it will help, I've got a thousand from the divorce settlement.'

'Dave, you can't.' I gave him a big hug. 'It wouldn't be fair, you'll need that money, the maintenance you're paying is high.'

He held me in his arms. 'That's life, everything comes at a price. Now come here, I've got half an hour to spare.'

~

I knew John would never agree to Dave putting money into the idea, but how else could we get the funds? It was such an opportunity and neither Dave nor I wanted to miss out on it. I spent another restless night, there were so many things happening at once. How had it got like this? Why did everything have to happen at the same time?

It was four in the morning and I continued to toss and turn. After battling the pillows for another fifteen minutes, I gave in, went into the kitchen and made a cup of tea. John was still asleep. I took the tea into the living room and looked out of the picture windows. The city lights were spread out below me; the heat rising in waves. We were experiencing the hottest summer for years. What a view, day or night. I could never imagine living anywhere without a view.

I sat down on the sofa and tried to work out a plan; nothing would come together. I placed Dianna Ross singing 'The Theme from Mahogany' on the turntable and sat back. An hour later, the notepad and pen remained untouched. I went back to bed.

~

The following morning, I wrote out my notice and handed it in. I had been taking time out to make the willy-warmers, which was not fair to a company that had always been fair with me.

Some of the girls were upset that I was leaving, yet not surprised. I was almost thirty-three and wanted a dog, which was impossible while working full-time, and I still missed Shep. It had been twelve years since she had died and memories of her still made me weepy.

I had made my decision; I could work from home and if everything failed with the willy-warmers and I had to go back out to work, I would only go part-time.

I tried to talk John into accepting the thousand pound offer from Dave.

'Jack, if we accept the money, then he's never going to go.'

I put down the cup I was holding. 'You're missing something, John. I don't want him to.'

He paced the flat. 'I thought this would be over when we finished your Mum and Dad's house.'

'Well, see what thought did.' I pushed my hands to my forehead. 'John, can't you see the opportunity?' I began following him around the flat. 'We can't raise the money on our own and if we could, we can't do the plumbing and heavy work that Dave does. Plus he's got that 'lecky-friend for the wiring.'

'I could get one of the electricians from work if it comes to that.'

My frustration was getting top-side of me.

'There's lots of things I don't like in life, John. It's not a perfect world and when it comes down to acquiring the better things in life – like nice clothes, high-powered cars and hotel holidays in the Caribbean, we as working class people are at the bottom of the pile for getting them. I proved it when I had that run-in with the union. I saw it with my Mum and the people she cleaned for. The few at the top take it all. You've only to look at the miners and Scargill. We've always had to work for what we've got, and damned hard too, like our parents and their parents before them, and how much better off did it get them? We are governed, John, kept by the ruling class. Our wages are fixed and always will be, we're at the bottom end of the system, we're not meant to have more. We're not academics, we weren't born into society with silver spoons and all that shit. We didn't go to college and university. This is an opportunity and you're letting your stupid pride get in the way.'

My temples were throbbing; I was out of breath and stood biting my nails, waiting for his response. It didn't take long; he walked out of the door.

'I'll tell you something, John,' I shouted after him. 'If we ever split over anything… it'll be over something like this and not another man.'

155

~

I left work the following Friday and had the leaving party in the pub next door. Even Ben Ellis came to see me off. After a few rounds of drinks and promises of coming back to see them after becoming a millionaire, when Ben Ellis would be expecting a gold lamé willy-warmer, it was time to say farewell. It was a happy, yet somewhat sad event. I had made a lot of friends at Globe and Simpson. Now something life-changing was happening, I didn't know what, but I knew I had to follow my gut instinct.

Chapter 28

There was no more talk about the house purchase and then one evening John came in from work with some large sheets of drawing paper. I didn't question the reason and just carried on finishing the dinner. After we had eaten – on the eight-by-four sheet of block-board, we couldn't be bothered to remove it now at meal times – I just brushed off the fluff and covered it with a table-cloth.

'Can I use the top half?' He was pointing towards the block-board.

'Yes,' I said. 'I can manage on this part.' I folded the tablecloth and placed it in the sideboard drawer.

'I've been doing some costing,' he said, placing his rule and some pens and pencils on the board. 'If Dave's willing to put up the thousand pounds, we can manage the remainder – though it will leave us short for buying materials, let alone other costs.'

All ears, I gave him a hug, pulled up a chair and sat down beside him.

'Submitting plans for the dormer window is going to cost – there will be solicitor's fees and then the electrician.'

'Do you want me get Dave over to work it out with you…?' As soon as I said it, I realised I shouldn't have. I went to the kitchen and washed the dishes.

~

The costs had been worked out as best as we could. Unless we sold more willy-warmers, we would struggle to pay for materials.

'Look, it's still summer, we could go to the seaside and sell some of the stock there,' said John. 'They have a big market on Sundays, at Ingoldmells, might be worth a try.'

The following Sunday morning, the intense heat had remained throughout the night. It was just coming light when we loaded the car with our stock and set off for Ingoldmells. It was seven in the morning when we arrived and joined the queue. Vans, lorries and cars were all pulling onto the site and jostling for the best spots, the site manager and stewards ushering the vehicles to their appropriate places. The ones who hadn't pre-booked space had to take pot luck in getting a good place, which included us.

There wasn't a spare inch of space in the car but eventually we unloaded and set up my pasting table with the willy-warmers displayed on top. John pegged some onto a piece of washing line he had strung above our heads. All set up, I went to find the beverage van and bought two mugs of tea. I took them back to our stand where we sat back on a couple of stools and waited for the crowds.

And they came, in unbelievable numbers. Hot and sweaty people and their overheated children were trudging around, one slow step after another; prams being shoved through baked dry ruts.

'What's a willy-warmer, Mum?'

'Can I have one, Dad?'

Laughing parents drew their offspring away, then nipped back to buy one.

By two o'clock, the hustle and bustle, screaming children and arguing parents had gone. Only the sound of stalls being dismantled, van and car doors slamming and the cows in the distant fields remained. By four o'clock, we were on our way home, having sold all our stock and also having found a couple of buyers with shops, who wanted regular supplies.

~

The bathroom at Mum and Dad's was finished. The deal with Graham Simpson was done and a contract was drawn up. With the money in place, all we needed now was a completion date. There was no reserve funding, so there was no room for error and nothing could go wrong.

158

I didn't quite catch up on my stock of willy-warmers and Ellen Toulson was making as many as she could, yet I was still behind. With both John and Dave cutting them in the evenings, they still weren't being sewn fast enough. I needed to be making them too but no longer had a machine.

I needed more fur-fabric and the chap on the market had not restocked his supplies and wouldn't be going until next week. That would be too late; they needed cutting now. I thought of going over to Rotherham or Barnsley market. John suggested that we needed to find out where the market trader got his fabric from.

'If we're going to be making larger supplies, we need to be buying it by the roll,' he said, and came in next evening with the Market Trader newspaper. He looked through it.

'There's one near Bradford and one at Oldham.'

We decided to stick with Yorkshire, and set off the following Sunday morning. I wound down the window in the car. It was a blistering hot day again, with tarmac melting on the roads.

'How long will it take?' I asked; my arm on the open window. I had never been to Bradford before and was quite excited, plus there was the prospect of warehouse shopping.

'Not long,' John replied. 'About an hour and a half.'

'*Young hearts run free.*' I began singing the current chart hit by Candi Staton as we pulled out of the car park.

~

Two hours later, we were in the Heaton area of Bradford.

'For God's sake, John, admit it. We're lost, and I don't like it.'

'We're not lost – I just need to get back on the 606,' he snapped, sweat running down the side of his face.

'Well ask someone.' I dabbed my forehead. The heat was unbearable, and the fan wasn't powerful enough for conditions like this. I had closed the window to shut out the awful smells that seemed to permeate from every road and street we turned into.

'I can't believe this is still Yorkshire, are you sure you haven't gone past it?'

'Jack, shut up. How can I concentrate with you nagging?'

'Please, John, let's go home.' I looked out of the window at the people, clothed all in black. 'Pull over, John, I'll ask someone, look there, that man with the woman. Surely they can see we're lost.' I wound down the window as john steered towards the kerb.

'Excuse me.'

They carried on walking. John kerb-crawled alongside until we were slightly ahead of them. I leaned my head out of the window.

'Excuse me,' I said again. 'Is this the way to the A606?'

They halted but didn't stop; they looked away and carried on walking.

I wound the window up as John pulled back into line.

'They'll not talk to you, Jack – it's a waste of time.'

Humiliated and upset, I looked down at my lap. John looked across and placed a hand on mine.

'As soon as I get back onto the A606, we'll go home, okay?'

My lip trembled. I nodded my head.

~

I kept quiet while John took various turns onto different roads.

'Aw fuck!'

Shocked, I looked up. 'What's the matter?' John never swore.

'It's a no-entry.'

He checked his mirror and looked over his shoulder. 'We can't go back, blast.'

His foot pushed down on the accelerator; the big engine roared.

Relieved to get to the top of the street, he turned left. There were even more crowds of people in black, brown and white gowns. Market stalls were set out on the street corners, elders sat on mats. The women all looked the same with their long black gowns and covered faces. I wondered how the children knew who their mothers were.

John drove as far as he dared; the last thing we wanted was to get stopped by the police here.

'This is it, Jack, we're back on the right road.' Relieved, John wiped the sweat from his face and continued along the road until we left the dense population behind. We opened the car windows again and enjoyed the welcoming breeze.

On the outskirts of Bradford I saw the sign.

'John, it's there, look.' I pointed to the left.

'Do you want to call in or go straight home?' he said as he slowed down.

'Might as well, now we can see it,' I said, having calmed down.

~

What a massive warehouse. I couldn't believe the size of it. We got out of the car, our clothes sticking to our backs as we stretched our legs in the shade. A Rolls Royce and a Daimler were parked near the entrance, along with large Bedford vans and a couple of furniture removal vans.

We shared a bottle of warm water and entered the loading bay as it appeared to be the only way in. We were quickly stopped. Two men appeared, dressed in black nightgowns with silly little hats on their heads.

'Customer entrance,' one of them said, with a foreign accent. He pointed to the other end of the building and ushered us away.

The small doorway for the customer entrance was around the corner and was locked. I rang the bell.

A foreign voice, which I couldn't understand, came from a speaker. We looked around but couldn't see anyone. I looked at John and shrugged.

'Hello, is anyone in?' I spoke into the speaker.

The voice crackled through the speaker again. 'Company name?'

'Sorry, I don't have one, we're new,' I replied.

Silence.

I saw a vertical blind move at a window and heard a buzz.

'Try the door,' said John. 'Someone's unlocked it.'

'Strange,' I whispered as I stepped inside. John followed.

The cool air inside the building was most welcome, and then my eyes widened in disbelief. There were rolls and rolls of fur fabric as far as I could see – to my left and right; all colours, and different qualities. Long pile, short pile, all stacked to the ceiling on heavy-duty racking.

'Have you ever seen anything like this?' I said to John, who was also taking it all in. A different man, wearing a similar black nightgown and hat came from a doorway on my left.

'Can I help you?'

'Er, yes. We're looking to buy some fur fabric.'

'Full rolls only, minimum sale twenty pounds,' he replied, his black beady eyes staring at John. He was probably wondering why the man wasn't doing the talking. 'Cash only!' he added.

A man of few words, I thought.

'How much is on a roll and what's the cost?' I asked, taking a step to one side so I was in front of him.

'Twenty-five to thirty yards, cost depends on quality.' He replied and walked away.

'I hope we haven't got to barter with him,' I mumbled to John. 'Just a minute,' I called after him and pulled a small piece of fur fabric from my handbag. 'This is what I'm looking for.'

He didn't touch the fabric; he looked at it and then me.

'What you pay for this?' he said.

'Three pounds for five yards,' I lied.

'Same price here,' he said and walked off.

John and I looked at each other and moved further into the building. Some spaces had been created between the racks, and photographs of foreign people who looked like rulers or some kind of holy men hung on the walls. I couldn't read what the inscriptions said, they were written in a different language. There were official notices too – I presumed they were official, as they looked it; there was nothing in English.

We continued walking around the wide shelves and saw what we needed.

'What do we do, help ourselves, or what?

'We can't pull these off the racks,' John replied and looked around to see if anyone was about. 'Hang on here,' he said. 'I'll have a walk down to the loading bay where those first two chaps were.'

I looked at the tag on the roll of red fabric: twenty-seven yards and then the blue: twenty-five.

John returned with one of the men, who yanked the two rolls off the shelves.

'You pay.' He pointed to the doorway where the boss had appeared from.

As we made our way to the office, I noticed about fifty rolls of different coloured fabrics, standing against the wall.

'John, look at that – it's perfect.' It was leopard print fur-fabric. 'Aw, I've got to have it. Can you see the willy-warmers made of that? They'll go down a bomb.'

I knocked on the office door.

'Pay,' I said, using the same abrupt speech. 'And one of these, please,' I added, pointing to the rolls of leopard, as the boss appeared.

'No, gone,' he replied, gesturing for me to move away from the rolls.

'What do you mean *gone*? It's there, isn't it, or am I seeing things?'

John nudged me and gave me a wide-eyed stare.

'Well, have you anymore?'

'No more, one month.'

A man came out of the office wearing a long brown mac. He was stuffing a large wad of notes into an inside pocket.

'Is Sajjad and Malik around to load up for me?' he asked the boss.

The boss called the two men, who came running over and started taking the rolls to the loading bay.

'Expecting rain?' I grinned. 'It is official, there is a drought.' I said to the man, while looking over his brown mac. 'You're English?'

'I was this morning when I got up, but anything can happen around here.' He laughed and slapped the boss on the back.

The boss gave a short condescending laugh.

The man in the mac turned to me and held out his hand. 'Bill Waite.'

What a grip. 'Careful with the hand, that's my cutting hand. I'm Jackie and this is my husband John.' He had a warm and friendly smile. I took to him straight away.

'What are you up to in the rag-trade?' he asked.

'What are *you* up to in the rag trade?'

'Soft toys, teddies, stuff like that. If it's an animal, I'll make a toy version.' We began walking towards the loading area; I stopped by the rolls of leopard fabric.

'What about this leopard material? What are you making with that?'

He laughed again. 'What do you think – Zebras?'

I looked away, grinning at my own stupidity.

'What do you want it for?'

'Just an idea, I'm working on it.' I tried to look nonchalant and slid a glance at John to keep shut.

'Come on, I'll let you have a roll.'

My eagerness betrayed me. 'Will you?'

'See you outside,' he winked. 'You'd better pay Mohammad for the red and blue.' He gestured towards the boss, who was waiting behind us.

~

Outside, Bill watched them load the furniture van with the rolls of fabric.

I left John to pay and joined Bill. 'Who are these people?'

'Pakistanis – they're okay, they keep themselves to themselves. They supply me with fabric, I pay them the money.'

'The boss wouldn't even look at me, probably thinks I should be at home cooking the Sunday dinner.'

'They don't think women should be involved in business matters.'

'Wha-a-at?'

'Yeah, you should be at home cooking, cleaning and keeping the bed warm, shouldn't she, John?' as John appeared.

164

I slapped his arm.

'Ouch.' He pulled a face.

'Not this one,' Bill said to one of the men and kept his hand on one of the large rolls of leopard.

'You must make a lot of toys,' I said, looking at the size of the van.

'I do. Come over sometime and have a look.'

'We will – whereabouts are you?'

'Conisborough, just outside Doncaster. Where's your place, or is that just an idea as well?'

'Cheeky,' I replied. 'Sheffield, Norfolk Park.'

'Oh! Have you got one of those units on East Bank Road?'

'Yeah!' I replied.

'Don't believe a word she tells you,' cut in John.

'John, he knows we haven't, stop being so serious.'

The two men finished loading Bill's van and slammed the doors. John made a move towards the car.

'Nearly forgot, Bill. How much for the fabric?' I said.

'Call it ten quid.' He walked towards John. 'Nice car, John, is it a one-twenty?'

'No, one-fifty, the one-twenty's got a split windscreen. How much did you say, Bill?'

'Ten.'

John opened the car doors to let the heat out and took out his wallet.

'Thanks, Bill.' he said, as he handed over the money.

'Anytime. Now, how are you going to get this lot in here?' he asked, adding the note to the wad in his deep pocket.

I got into the back, behind the driver's seat and fanned my face with the AA road map. John pushed two rolls of fabric alongside me.

'You'll not get three in,' said Bill, weighing up the situation. I got back out of the car.

'I'm not leaving that one,' I said, looking at the roll of leopard.

'Let's get them out,' said Bill. 'I'll put them in the van – you can follow me back if you want or come over later – my wheels aren't as fast as yours.'

As much as I liked Bill, I was reluctant to see the roll of leopard vanish into the back of his van with the red and blue. It was impossible to get all three rolls in, so we promised to go over the following afternoon. John had a few hours owing and he could borrow a van from work.

We enjoyed the beautiful Yorkshire countryside as we made our way back to Sheffield, leaving Bill and his van a long way behind. I liked Bill and was looking forward to going over to his place. My mind was full of ideas for the leopard fabric and I knew the new willy-warmers would be big sellers. My life was certainly changing, and not only my life, as I recalled the incident in Bradford. The country was changing too.

Chapter 29

Bill's factory was enormous. He had a large area racked with metal shelving, holding rolls of fur fabric. Adjoining it was a cutting area, where two twenty-foot-long and eight-foot-wide cutting tables were placed, both with automatic fabric layering machines and overhead wires for the cutters to run from. A smaller table was nearby, with a hydraulic press which cut out smaller components from metal dies, up to ten layers at a time.

'That's what we could do with for cutting out the willy-warmers,' I said to John, who was taking in the layout. A gigantic cylinder, which looked like a farming silo stood in one corner and held the filling material. Two youths were at work, continuously filling the furry animals. As each container of toys filled, someone wheeled it away, replacing it with an empty one. Giant tortoises and dogs for children to sit on waited in line. There were zebras, giraffes, elephants and hippos in every colour imaginable, along with various teddy bears, Rupert Bears and Paddington Bears. A large container held hundreds of Wombles. Scooby-Doo and Felix were amongst other characters piled in massive containers. What a place!

We entered a large open entrance into another area where the machinists sat in rows, all working on industrial sewing machines. Abba were singing 'Mamma Mia' over the speaker system, which had no problem competing with the noise of the machines. The machinists all looked happy as they pushed endless animal parts through their machines.

'What do you think?' asked Bill as he handed us mugs of tea.

'Bill, it's fantastic, I'm just mesmerized, it makes our place look smaller still.'

We moved to a quieter area as the record changed and all the machinists began singing along with The Shangri-Las and 'Leader of the Pack'. We sat at a table in the canteen.

'So how big is your place then?' asked Bill.

I looked down at my hands.

'It isn't a place at all, Bill.' I looked at John. 'We work from home.' I looked straight across at him. His friendly eyes twinkled.

'So? We all have to start somewhere. What are you thinking of making?' He took a gulp of tea.

I looked at John and then back at Bill.

'Willy-warmers,' I said, and looked away.

He burst out laughing; his tea spilled over the mug.

'Ah! The leopard fabric, that figures.' He sat considering it, grinning. 'Who dreamed that up?' He looked across at us.

'Me,' I said, and took one from my handbag to show him.

He laughed again and shook his head as he took it from me. 'So who cuts these?'

'We do, on a piece of eight-by-four on the dining room table.'

'On the dining-room table?'

'Yes, it's better than the floor.'

'You could do with a press, and stamp them out.'

'We don't have much room – we live in a council flat.'

'You'll have to watch it. If the council gets to know, they'll be on to you.'

'How old are you, John, if you don't mind me asking?'

'Thirty-six next month,' John replied.

'Don't let the years creep up on you. If you're going to buy a house, you need to be thinking about it now. You'll not get a mortgage once you get to forty.'

'We don't want to buy a house, we're happy in the flat, and why can't you get a mortgage when you're forty?' I asked.

'Well that's if you're taking out a twenty-five year one…'

168

'What? A twenty-five year mortgage – I can't see us living that long with the life we live.'

'You never know.' He looked serious. 'If the business takes off, you might change your mind, and the lenders will not take your earnings into account, Jackie.' He looked at me and raised his eyebrows. 'Even if you do become the breadwinner. Do you want any more tea?'

We were deep in thought with all we had seen and what he had said. 'Thanks, Bill, none for me,' I said and John agreed. We stood up to leave.

'Look, keep in touch. If there's anything I can help you with, let me know. And if you want me to get a die made, I can stamp out the willy-warmers for you.

'Don't know about the stamp, Bill. I'd love an industrial machine though, when I can afford one.'

'I've some older ones in the back. I'll find one out for you.'

I gave Bill a hug and we left.

~

The following day, we had a letter from the solicitor, stating that a completion date had been arranged for Monday 23rd August. Which was fine by us – the money was in place, we just needed to get on with the plans for the dormer window. John had drawn up the plans and we just needed final checks of the sizes before submitting.

'What do you want for your birthday?' John asked, as we were packing some cut willy-warmers for Ellen Toulson.

'If I can't have a factory like Bill's, what about a baby?'

John stopped packing and stared at me.

'Are you serious?'

I couldn't make out what he was thinking. I smiled.

'Yes, why not now I'm working from home? I'm thirty-three in three weeks, and you know I've always wanted one since losing Shep.'

He looked somehow relieved. 'Ah, you mean a four-legged one?'

'Of course! You didn't think I meant the other type, did you? Definitely not, you lose your identity when you start having them. It wouldn't be so bad if they stayed babies, but they don't, they grow up into ever-demanding adults. I love to cuddle and hold them and then give them back.'

I thought of my mum and John's mum, and all my Aunties and everyone else I knew who'd had babies.

'No, give me a pup any day.' We resumed packing the sewing work for Ellen.

~

We couldn't stop talking about Bill's factory. 'I'll have to ask him how old he was when he set up his business. How old do you think he is?'

'Not much older than us – late thirties, early forties, I reckon.' John replied.

We were on our way to Platts Common, a suburb of Barnsley, about fifteen miles north-east of Sheffield. I had seen an advert in the Sheffield Star for an Old English sheepdog, with a genuine reason for the sale. The house was in a street similar to Mum's and we parked outside and knocked on the door. Dogs barked. 'Perhaps we should have gone to the back,' I said.

The door opened and a man, probably in his fifties, asked us in. He led us through to the kitchen, where we were greeted by an over-friendly dog with a coat of blackish grey wool. He was prancing about all over the place and, without a tail, it was difficult to tell which end was which. Another smaller dog was darting in and out beneath him.

'He's beautiful, what's his name?'

'Toby – he's just a bit too big for us, we didn't realise he would grow as big as this.'

'Toby,' I said. 'Come here, boy.' He was too giddy to hold. 'How old did you say he was?'

'He's just six months – he's had all his injections and things.'

I managed to grab hold of hyper-active Toby. I was surprised.

'He's got blue eyes.' I'd never seen a blue-eyed dog before. 'Will they turn brown?'

'They'll stay blue, they'll not change now. Stop that, Jake.'

The small dog, a Jack Russell, appeared from beneath Toby and nipped his leg.

I knelt on the carpet.

'Ooh, you're naughty, aren't you?' I said, as the little fellow backed away.

Toby turned on unsteady legs and tried to find the culprit, sneaky Jake, older than the big pup and knew he could hide beneath him.

'You can see what happens, can't you?' said the man, trying to get the little dog from underneath Toby.

'He's just jealous, aren't you?' said the man's wife. She bent down and picked the little fellow up.

We talked for a while about where we lived and the different areas of Sheffield. They said they never went into Sheffield as Barnsley had all their needs. I could never imagine living in a small town after a city – I would hate it. We declined another cup of tea and said we had to be on our way.

'Are you coming with us then, Toby?' Toby was more interested in where the little one had got to. 'How much did you say? Forty pounds?'

John took forty pounds from his wallet and handed it over.

We said our goodbyes as I took hold of Toby's lead and walked him to the car.

'Goodbye and thank you, he'll have a good home. I promise.'

John opened the car door and I got into the back. Toby tried to jump in after me and failed; he couldn't get his legs to co-ordinate. He finally settled on the back seat with me and John pulled away. I waved farewell to Mr and Mrs Williams and looked at my baby.

'You're mine now.' I gave him a big hug. 'I'm renaming you Muffin.'

Chapter 30

It was nearly tea-time. I was tidying away after cutting all afternoon. I looked around at my once- lovely flat. Now it was covered in bits of fur fabric. Every room held boxes, ribbons and sewing threads. A large industrial sewing machine that Bill had let me have sat at the end of the hall. It was old, yet reliable and fast. It stood on an inch-thick felt pad, as Bill said it would be necessary with our concrete floors and residents living below.

I gave Muffin his tea and covered and set the block-board for ours. I turned the oven off: the pie had finished cooking and as the oven was electric; it would keep warm till John arrived. The kettle was filled. Looking through the living room window, I stroked Muffin's head as he sat on the settee. He was a lovely dog, still gangly, his Old English shape not yet in place. I kissed his head as we waited for John. Dave had been around earlier and sometimes he stayed for dinner; John didn't like it.

I looked out of the window again. Where had he got to? He was late and I could usually hear the car's engine by now.

The phone rang, which made me jump. I ran down the hallway.

'Hello!'

'Jack, it's me. The car's broke down.'

'John, are you all right? What's happened?' Relieved he was okay, I listened. Muffin came and sat by my feet.

'The spokes have gone on the wheels.'

'I don't know what you mean.'

'They've collapsed. Look, I'll tell you more when I get home – I'm going to get the bus.'

I switched the oven back on and waited. Forty minutes later, he arrived. I served the meat and potato pie with peas and gravy and sat down.

'So what does it mean?' I asked. 'Is it serious?'

'Serious enough,' he replied, while pulling all the pieces of meat out of the pie and inspecting them.

'John, I made it. I've removed all traces of fat and gristle, now get on with it,' I snapped.

'Okay, I'm just checking.'

'Well, don't. Otherwise, you can make your own in future, or buy one. Then you haven't got a clue what you're eating. What about the car?'

'I've phoned Dennis – he's going to see what he can do, he'll ring me later.'

We sat in silence while finishing our dinner. John said he would wash the dishes and wait for the phone call while I took Muffin a walk. I phoned Dave and said I would meet him in the basement. Muffin and I ran down all fifteen floors. I told Dave about the car as walked around the park. We played ball with Muffin and practiced his obedience training, then called into the pub for a drink before going home.

John was silent when we returned; I was slightly out of breath after walking back up the fifteen floors.

'What did Dennis have to say?' I drank a glass of water and sat down.

'Not good news. Dennis can't fix it.' He looked at me, his face showing concern. 'The wheels need re-spoking, it's a specialized job.' He stood up and looked out of the window. 'He's going to let me know more tomorrow.'

~

'We can't afford it, Jack, our spare money is with the solicitor for the house.'

'There must be something we can do, John.' I clenched and unclenched my hands while thinking, and then resorted to nail-biting.

'Dennis is looking to see if he can find anything that will do. I doubt if he'll find four replacement wheels that we can afford.'

'Why have we never got any money when we need it?' I was pacing the flat, Muffin following me.

'Jack, our money's tied up in stock and the house. You can't have your cake and eat it.'

'Who says?' I snapped. 'Some people seem to.'

'Stop it, Jack, you're only upsetting yourself.' He took hold of me and gave me a cuddle.

'But it's not fair – you can't sell the car without the wheels and we can't afford to get them done.' Muffin came over to join in the cuddles.

I suddenly had an idea.

'I know what, I'll ask Mum. We've never asked Mum for anything and she must have some savings with not having to pay rent.'

'I'm not sure about that, Jack.'

'John, we would only be borrowing it, she's helped Ian out enough and perhaps it's our turn now. I'll go down and see her tomorrow.'

'We'll have to go on the bus.'

~

'What do you mean you haven't any savings? What about the money you were going to save by not paying rent?' I was furious. She was drunk and in a nasty mood.

'It's nothing to do with you where my money's gone, so don't come asking. I don't ask you about your money.' Her words were slurred.

'Where's your Post Office savings book?' I snapped and went to the sideboard cupboard where I knew she kept it.

She flew at me, raging. 'Keep out of my affairs!' she screamed, her lips turning blue.

I was worried that she might have a heart attack

174

'Look, Mum, calm down and sit down. I've every right to know.' I took hold of her wrists and settled her into her chair. 'Now, let's talk about this sensibly. Do you want a cup of coffee?'

'You can't bribe me with coffee. I know what you're trying to do.'

'I could bribe you with a Gold Label though, couldn't I?' She went quiet. 'What am I trying to do, huh? Tell me?'

She stared at me unsteadily.

'Go away, I don't want you coming here, upsetting me and your dad.'

'Dad's not here, he's in the front room.' I needed to get to the bottom of this and wasn't leaving till I had. John had said he would come with me, but I knew it might come to this and John would be urging me to leave. Mum's strong reaction to my wanting to know about her money made me even more suspicious.

'Has Ian been taking your money? You might as well tell me, I'll find out somehow, in fact I'll go round when I leave here and tell him *you* told me about the money he's taken.'

'Ian has not taken my money, I've given it him. He's got enough on his plate without a job and a baby on the way, and you, you bugger, wouldn't let them live here. So stay away from him.'

'Stay away from him? I'll smash his bloody head in when I see him.'

Her temper flared again. She pulled herself out of the chair and came at me like a mad dog. Muffin, who was with me, jumped up and started barking at her.

'And you shut up,' she said to him. Her eyes blazed and her fists were clenched.

I wanted to scream.

Chapter 31

The Jag was advertised in *Classic Cars* magazine and sold at a loss, and all we could afford was an old van; at least we had wheels. We now owned twenty-six Tanfield Road and a lot of work lay ahead of us. Ideally, we wanted to start at the top of the house; as we couldn't do anything until planning consent came through for the dormer window, we did what we could.

The old fireplaces were removed, along with the contents of the cellar. Having the old van turned out to be a good idea with all the rubbish that needed removing. We had the radio on and Dave whistled and I sang along with the Bee Gees to 'Night Fever'. John worked methodically on his project. It wasn't long before my hands took on the appearance of a bricky's again as we worked flat-out before the winter settled in.

Every evening after dinner and at weekends, we made our way down to the house with Dave and did our best. Muffin came with us, the four of squashed together on the bench seat in the front of the van. He climbed up and down the stairs in the house, and enjoyed a run around Hillsborough Park if it was still light enough when we were ready to leave. He did get in our way many times, but it was nothing Dave and I couldn't cope with. John, on the other hand, was forever moaning that he would get splinters and nails in his paws. Whatever, I'd take my chances: it was better than leaving him at home.

I didn't speak to Mum and only went in to see Dad when she wasn't around. She popped in occasionally to see how far we had got. When I told John about the argument over the money, he told me to ignore it; it was her money and what she did with it was up to her. I was as mad with him as her.

By Christmas, we had made good progress on the house and reckoned it would be finished by next summer. Planning consent had come through and the building inspector checked our progress. We took Christmas day off and I cooked roast turkey with all the trimmings. Dave joined us and ate a hearty plateful, along with mine and John's leftovers. I opened a bottle of Mateus Rose, which I had bought because of the shape of the bottle and took an instant liking to the contents too. We drank a toast to the coming year; even John and Dave clinked glasses.

John and I took Muffin to the park afterwards while Dave washed the dishes. As the afternoon wore on, with the TV turned down low, John dozed in his chair, so did Dave on the settee, and I lay on the floor with Muffin, watching the silver Christmas tree shimmer, its lights filling the room with a soft glow. A basket of pines cones, dried flowers and wood shavings were placed in a corner and with the heat from the floor, filled the air with the scent of cinnamon, frankincense and myrrh. Peace at Christmas.

As Christmas Day and Boxing Day had fallen over the weekend, John and Dave had two extra days holiday, and used them to work on the house. We also called in to see Mum and Dad and take them their Christmas presents, and called round to see Lynda and Ian who were renting a house in the next street. Jo and Brian sufficed with a phone call and a promise to see them in the New Year.

~

On the first weekend in the New Year, John and I went to see Jo and Brian. They made a big fuss of Muffin and he lapped it up, the big softy. They lived in Beauchief, a smart suburban area of Sheffield. Their house was lovely: a modern semi-detached with a bay window and back and front gardens with daffodils and snowdrops already poking through the black soil. After they had shown us around the house, we sat on a beige Parker Knoll sofa, drinking coffee from a machine not unlike the ones in cafés.

We hadn't sat down for long when we heard a knock on the door.

'I'll go,' said Brian. He came back after a minute. 'John, would you move the van, please? Most of it is parked in front of our neighbour's house.'

John got up straight away and felt in his pocket for the keys.

'He's funny like that,' said Brian as John passed him.

I watched through the window as John drove the van about another three feet forward and came back in. We both looked at each other with a raised eyebrow. He sat down.

'Doesn't it scare you, having a twenty-five year mortgage?' I asked, as Jo and Brian resumed their places.

'Not really,' said Jo, in her usual nonchalant manner.

'What's the point in having a posh house if you can't afford to go out and on holiday?'

They just shrugged. I could tell they didn't want to talk about money issues so I asked why they were having a change of career, which Mum had already explained the reason for, and now they confirmed it.

'I can see Brian as department manager, Jo, but I can't see you as an office clerk. Have you learned to type?'

She looked down at her beautiful hands and fingernails.

'What, with my nails? Not likely. Typing would ruin them.'

Jo's hands and fingernails were the opposite of mine. She had once won a "Miss Beautiful Hands" competition and had been given a manicure set in a leather case, along with nail and hand-treatment vouchers. A misty black and white photograph of her hands, framed in pewter, stood on the room divider, along with her wedding photo. I looked down at my bricky's hands. Ah well!

'Don't office clerks have to have typing skills?' I asked. 'They did when I worked in an office.'

'No, we can fill forms in by hand,' she replied.

'It'll take forever by longhand, Jo.'

'Government-run,' said John. 'Tax-payers are paying, so time doesn't matter.'

Brian laughed.

I asked Jo if they had any plans for children. At this question, Brian and John departed into another area of conversation.

'Yes, nothing's happened yet,' she replied, looking down at her hands again.

'Lynda's showing now,' I said. 'Reckons it's a boy. I don't how they can tell, do you?'

'No, yet I'd love the experience.' Misty eyed, she looked towards the window.'

'Look on the bright side, Jo, look how much fun you're having while trying.'

She gave a forced, weak laugh. We stayed for about an hour. Muffin decided he'd had enough and so had we. We promised to see them before Easter and left them with their heavily-mortgaged house.

'I couldn't sleep at night if I'd got a debt like that, could you?' I said to John on our way home.

'Nor neighbours like theirs either,' he replied.

Chapter 32

Spring came, and the house was almost complete. We were debating what price we should market the house at, as we needed a quick sale.

All our capital had gone and it was too early in the season to take the willy-warmers to the seaside, plus we needed a reliable vehicle to get them there, not the clapped-out old van we had put up with for the last few months.

The renovations had been passed by the building inspector, and we asked a property dealer to check it over and give a sales figure. A smartly dressed middle-aged chap came along with his clipboard and wrote down measurements and other particulars. His findings were that it was definitely mortgageable, with a valuation figure of five to five and a half thousand pounds, which was what we expected. I was pleased and proud of the work we had done and said I would get back to him regarding his offer of selling it on our behalf.

Before we decided on a figure, Ann Smith, an old friend of Jo's, who still lived in the street, came over and asked what we would sell it for. She was now married with a baby, and the three of them lived with her mother and father.

A deal was done. We used the same solicitor who had dealt with our purchase.

~

We were rich. John didn't dash out and buy a flash car. Instead, he wisely said that we would need one good on petrol if we intended to carry on selling our goods at the seaside. We decided on another van, a newer one.

We chose a Volkswagen Transporter: a panel van with a 1,600cc engine. I phoned Norwich Union with all the details to change the insurance.

'I'll have to ring you back, Mrs Creek. I need to check something with the head clerk before I can give you a quote.'

'That's okay – I'll be in all day,' I replied and returned to my eight-by-four table, where I was designing packaging for the willy-warmers. The retailers had complained that they were having difficulties displaying them, so I decided to place them in individual polythene bags with a display header, with a hole-punched in the centre for hanging. I reckoned I could get three headers from a sheet of A4, which John said he could get copied and printed at work. I was completing the design when the phone rang again.

'Hello, Mrs Creek? It's Adele from Norwich Union, I spoke to you earlier.'

'Yes, I remember, Adele, what have you found out?'

'I need to know the maximum amount of vehicles it will carry?'

'Huh? It's a van, it doesn't carry vehicles.'

'You said it was a transporter.'

'Yes, that's the name of the model…a Volkswagen Transporter panel van – I did state it was a van – 1,600cc.'

'There must be some mistake, it's listed as a vehicle transporting vehicle…'

'Look, can you get back to your head clerk and tell him to look into it, I'm busy.'

"LUXURY WILLY WARMER"
One Size Fits All

I held up the header.

'Yes, that's perfect,' I said to myself.

'What is?' asked John, coming in from work.

'The label – look.' I held it in front of him.

'I like it, not sure about the one size fits all, though.'

'I know, that's the plan. Men being men…'

The phone rang again.

'You take it, John. If it's from Norwich Union again, tell them we're changing insurance companies.' I looked hard at the label. *Hmm.*

He came back into the room.

'Didn't you tell them it was a van? They think it's a car transporter…what's for tea?'

'Idiots! Of course I told them. I've got some liver and onions with mash if that's okay.'

'That will do – make sure you remove all the sinewy bits.'

'Yes, love,' I replied. 'Just being the good little housewife that I am.' I put my tongue in my cheek and went into the kitchen.

He kept looking over at the label that had been pushed to the top of the table, surrounded with pens, pencils, crayons and sheets of A4 paper.

'I think you've got something with that,' he said.

'So do I – and I think we ought to make a larger one.' I placed my knife and fork on the plate and picked up my cup.

'A larger one, as in what?' he looked puzzled.

'As I was saying earlier – men, being men, will not accept that one size fits all. So why don't we make a larger one…as in – Blackpool Donkey?'

~

The following day, John was at work and I managed to get the insurance sorted. My mind, as usual, was overflowing with ideas, especially for the extra-large willy-warmers.

I drew a new pattern on a sheet of brown paper. Just then, the outer door opened.

Only Dave's presence could intercept my thoughts in such a way that made me want to cast my clothes aside and feel his hard strong body pressed against me. Within minutes, we were in bed, indulging in our stolen moments, as the all-consuming need for love and sexual gratification once again tore through our entwined bodies, between damp and clinging sheets.

~

'That looks interesting,' said Dave, half an hour later, as he came from the bathroom and looked at the piece of brown paper on the Contiboard.

My libido sated, I told him of the plan.

'Why haven't you made an extra-large pattern?' He grinned.

'Ha-ha, very funny. I think they should sell well in Blackpool.'

'I'm sure they will,' he replied.

The letter box rattled so I went to pick up the mail. My limbs ached. One was a letter from Sheffield Council.

Dear Mr and Mrs Creek, it has come to our notice…

What the…?

'Dave, look at this.'

I was furious. The phone rang. Handing Dave the letter, I stormed along the hallway to answer it.

'Hello,' I snapped. 'No, I don't want any double glazing, thanks and if you can fit it in these windows, you'll be damn lucky.'

'Whatever next?' I said to Dave as I returned. 'Fifteen storeys high and they want to fit double glazing!'

'Easy,' he replied, looking up from the letter. 'They do it from the inside.'

I suddenly realised my gaff and was even angrier.

'Do you know your eyes turn turquoise when you're mad?' He put down the letter and took me in his arms.

'And yours will turn black if you don't let me get on with some work.'

He laughed and held me tighter. I wrapped my arms around him; he nibbled my ear.

'What do you think about the letter?'

'Ignore it, they'll not do anything, they'll not get off their backsides for a start, now come here, I've got half an hour left.' He began walking backwards, taking me with him towards the bedroom.

~

I showed John the letter when he came home from work.

'I'm not having them accusing Muffin of something he's never done. He's never done anything like that and even if he did have an accident, I'd clean it up.'

183

John didn't reply. He was thinking. I went into the kitchen and took the meat and potato pie from the oven, placed it on the worktop and went back into the room.

'It's the slum clearance people they're moving into the flats of late – they're the ones who are peeing in the lifts and basement.' I stormed back into the kitchen, took out a serving spoon and slammed the drawer shut.

We ate in silence.

'Do you think someone's reported us?' I suddenly said. 'If they have, I'll give them something to complain about when I get another a dog.'

He stopped chewing.

'Jack, you can't get another dog, one's enough and he's a big dog.'

'One might be enough for you but it isn't for me.' Seething, I sat quiet.

'Is this a bought pie?' asked John, as he put down his knife and fork and pushed his plate to one side. He pulled a piece of gristle from his mouth.

I felt guilty and looked down at my plate.

'Yes, I didn't have time to stew the meat and make the pastry. Do you want me to get you something else – there's some steak in the fridge.

'No, I'll get some beans on toast.'

~

The following evening, we were watching a repeat of *Rising Damp* on TV.

'Jack, I've been thinking about the letter and other things.'

'What other things?' I replied, emphasizing the last syllable and still watching the TV. I laughed as Rigsby tried to seduce Miss Jones with a piece of burning wood after following Philip's advice on how to attract a woman.

'Like when Bill Waite said we ought to buy a house while I can still get a mortgage.'

'I don't want a mortgage – it's a hell of a debt.' I stroked Muffin's head, then bent over and kissed it. 'We don't want to move, do we,

Muffin? We like it here near to the park.' I looked up at John, hoping he'd got the point. 'Besides, we'll never be able to afford to go out – look at Jo and Brian – lovely house and can't afford to go anywhere.'

'With the money we've made on the house renovation, we can put down a higher deposit, so the monthly payments will be less.'

I looked at him. 'John, it's not all our money – some of it's Dave's.'

He raised his eyebrows. 'Hasn't he got his cut yet?'

'Well, no. He told me to hang on to it in case we bought another – says he knows where it is if he needs it.'

John was angry. I looked back at the TV.

An atmosphere hung in the air again as John looked through the evening paper for properties, and I asked for the Pets for Sale page.

~

It was almost time for the holiday season to begin and we checked our stock levels: they were good, and Ellen Toulson was still happy to sew them.

As we would be staying overnight, Dave said he would look after Muffin for the weekend. On Saturday morning, John and I set off in the loaded up van for the East Coast. Ideally, we wanted to cover Skegness, Mablethorpe and Cleethorpes, before taking the long route around the River Humber and heading to Scarborough and Bridlington, leaving the West Coast until the following weekend.

It was a good and bad weekend. We sold most of the stock, yet didn't receive payment from a lot of customers as it was the start of the season and no funds were available. They placed further orders for the following month and said that was when payment would be made for the first consignment, when we delivered again. Which was okay with us, although we would have preferred cash on delivery. However, if this was how businesses were run and we needed to sell our stock first, then so be it.

The season went well. June was the bumper sales month, with the retailers stocking up for the main holiday period – July and August. As the holiday season came to a close, we left early one Saturday in mid-September, excited by the amount of money we stood to collect. When we arrived in Skegness, our enthusiasm was short-lived; most of the shops were closed when we arrived. We asked in a café that was still open.

'They've shut for the season, love. When the kids go back to school, they shut up shop and take their holidays. Most of them will be in the Caribbean or the Canaries by now.'

Upset and angry, I turned away. John put his arm around me.

'Come on, Jack, we'll come back next year.'

'You can, I'm not.' I pushed his arm from around me and hurried out of the cafe.

He caught up with me.

'Jack, don't upset yourself, there's nothing we can do.'

'Nothing we can do! Nothing we can do!' I shouted at him. 'There's plenty we can bloody-well do, I'll find a rag and a can of petrol and shove it through their letter boxes – at least I'd feel better.' I stormed off again along the prom, the easterly wind blowing in from the sea, with its spray and cold rain.

He caught hold of my arm and spun me round.

'Let go!' I snapped.

'It's not my fault, Jack.'

'It's not mine either. All that money we've spent and we've hardly recouped any.'

'Come on, we'll go on up to Mablethorpe. We might have better luck there. Shall we get some fish and chips before we go?'

I kicked the pavement.

'Might as well, I suppose.'

Chapter 33

We received about half the money we were owed on the East Coast. Blackpool, the following week fared much better as the shops were still open. They continued selling, as it was still a busy time for them, with the illuminations.

On our way home, fate played a hand. There were roadworks and diversions in place and we missed our turn-off towards the east and arrived in Manchester. Trying to find our way back out, we ended up in the wholesalers' area of Cheetham Hill. Driving around, looking for signs for Belle Vue, we saw a large building with colourful characters painted on the outside. We pulled up and walked around the outside of the building. Holding on to the security railings, we peered through the top of the windows which hadn't been painted out.

'It's a jokes and novelties wholesaler. Do you think they'd be interested in the willy-warmers?'

'I don't see why not,' John replied.

I climbed into the front of the van while John looked in the back. He reappeared with half a dozen willy-warmers.

'What about a price? They'll want their cut too.' He let go of the door handle.

'They usually work on a 25 to 33% profit margin.'

'Can we afford to drop our prices though?'

'Let's put it this way, you've only one place to collect payment from.' He raised his eyebrows. 'And travelling to Manchester is not like travelling to the coastal regions – he can supply a lot more shops than we can. Look at the cars and vans parked around the building and the car park's full.'

'Hmm! I think it's worth a try a try – let's go in and see.'

We made our way towards the large doors: STRICTLY WHOLESALE – £20 MINIMUM SPEND. We looked at the notice, then at each other and entered.

Hats, wigs and masks, grass skirts, flags and bunting covered the walls. Jokes, novelties and smaller items of every description filled the shelves. Fart cushions, black face soap, squirting flowers, jumping beans, novelty key rings, balloons of every shape and size, itching powder and sneezing powder. Rows and rows of humorous merchandise lined either side of the aisles.

To the left of the far aisle was another large room, stacked floor to ceiling with boxes of every dimension. Two lads were busy packing goods, labelling the boxes and placing them by a large roll-up steel shutter door, which I presumed would be a collection point for the couriers tomorrow. It was a fun palace.

We made our way to the counter. Six people were taking goods from overloaded trolleys; the counter staff checking the prices into the tills.

'Cash, cheque or account?' they asked, as the items were registered into the tills and reloaded onto other trolleys for taking to the vehicles parked outside.

'Can I help you?' asked a girl behind the counter. She was wearing a black felt hat, an eye mask and a Zorro cape.

'Er, yes. Is the proprietor in, please?'

'He is – he's busy with someone at the moment.'

Someone was pushing from behind, eager to get to the counter, pay for his stock and get off home. The cool afternoon sun had disappeared and it was dropping dark.

'Will it be okay if we wait?' I asked.

'Yes, what are your names? Feel free to look around – the trolleys are by the large doors. There's a couple of lads knocking about if you need anything lifting from the higher shelves.'

188

I smiled, told her our names and thanked her, then moved out of the way of the anxious retailers.

'What a place. Have you ever seen anything like this before?'

'No,' John replied. 'Let's see if there's a cheeky corner anywhere.'

'Okay, you take that side and I'll take this.' Fascinated by the merchandise on display, I wandered down the aisle. A set of wind-up false teeth were chattering away on top of a display box.

I picked up a tin cylinder and read the label: *Glow in the dark peanuts – ideal for eating in the cinema.* Curious, I lifted the lid. WHOOSH! Out jumped a squeaking snake on a spring. I pressed my hand to my chest, and then saw the funny side as other shoppers began laughing.

I moved on down the line, looking and not opening anything. When I reached the end, I looked to see if I could see John. He must have gone down another aisle. Just as I turned, I saw the saucy section. Playing cards, backed with photographs of nudes. Big Bertha bloomers, Beer glasses with nude images in the bottom, Booby mugs, Willy-worms: *Grow your own willies – drop them in water and see how they grow.* Whatever next, I thought. I picked up a kaleidoscope: *See the unbelievable – Never before seen by the human eye – you will be mystified.*

Fascinated, I placed the tube to my right eye and turned the outer tube. Nothing. I held it closer and turned it again. Still nothing – must be faulty, I thought and tried another: same again. I turned around, looking for John to see if he could see anything in it. A man and a woman were passing and burst out laughing, someone else did as I went in search of John.

'You've not been here before then?' said a man with a big grin across his face.

'No, why?' I said, wondering why he would ask. 'Are you the owner?'

John appeared before the man could answer. I passed him the kaleidoscope.

'Can you see…?' John and the man looked at each other and laughed. 'What's so funny?' I was getting annoyed.

'Here,' said the man. He took a mirror from one of the shelves and handed it to me. A screeching laugh came from it as I stared at the big black rings around my eyes. I reached in my handbag for a hanky.

'Here, let me do it,' said John, as he took the hanky from me and began to wipe my eyes, much to the amusement of the passers-by.

Trying to cover my face, I made my way to the counter and asked Zorro if there was a toilet I could use. Laughing at my red and black smeared face, she pointed to the Ladies' room.

Cleaning myself up as best as I could, I couldn't help laughing at my gullibility. I made my way back into the warehouse to find John talking to the man who had handed me the mirror.

The man laughed again when he saw me. I looked away, embarrassed and grinning. He put his arm around me.

'Your husband's been showing me your willy-warmers. Good product, I'll definitely have some. I'm sure Meir will take some. He had some of the little knitted ones a while since – they didn't sell. I'm sure these will be a money-spinner though.'

'Will Mr and Mrs Creek come to the front desk, please?' A voice came over the Tannoy.

'That's us.' We said goodbye to the chap and began to make our way to the counter.

'Good luck – I'm sure you don't need it.' He smiled and raised his hand.

Zorro grinned again when she saw me.

'Mr Cohen will see you now – that's his office.' She pointed behind her and carried on serving.

There was a glass partition, so the office wasn't visibly private. We knocked and entered.

He was waiting for us, his hand outstretched in greeting. Speaking our names, he introduced himself.

190

'Meir Cohen, at your service. Now, I believe you wish to open an account.' He spoke with a broad Mancunian accent, which betrayed the small black skull-cap on the back of his head.

John and I looked at each other.

'Please, excuse my manners, do sit down. Would you like tea or coffee?' He pressed a bell on his desk and someone appeared from an internal door. 'This is my wife Maya, same name but spelled differently.'

Maya came over and shook our hands. She was small and pretty.

'What would you like to drink?' she asked in a non-Mancunian accent

'Tea for me please.' I wondered how they had got into a business like this.

'Same for me please,' said John.

She left the room, quietly closing the door behind her.

'Right, let's get down to business,' said Meir as he settled himself behind his desk. 'How long have you been trading? I will need references, of course.'

I looked at John, who gave a slight shake of his head. I didn't know whether he meant he didn't want to talk or whether he wanted me to shut up.

'Mr Cohen…' John interrupted.

'Meir, please.' He gestured for me to carry on.

'We don't have a shop, Mr…Meir – I make willy-warmers.'

'Willy-warmers?' He looked surprised.

'We have only just started making them and wondered if you would be interested in stocking them.'

John opened the carrier bag and placed the only six we had with us on his desk. Meir picked one up and laughed.

'Who's idea was this?' he said, looking at both of us. 'Say, Maya, what do you think to these?' he said, as his wife entered carrying a tray. She placed it on the desk.

'Ooh! Yes, I like the leopard one. Do you make these?' She looked at me and then John.

'Yes,' I nodded, all of us sharing the humour.

'I think you would have to make a larger one for Meir,' she said. 'I thought I would say it before you, Meir.' She looked at him and laughed, then turned towards us. 'Help yourselves to milk and sugar.' She nodded towards the tray, and left the room.

I don't know why I was surprised. I thought of the range of stock they carried, yet their sense of humour was the same as ours. I remembered my mum telling me about when she went into service at the age of thirteen and was sent to Leeds to work for a Jewish family. She said they were lovely people, with a good sense of right and wrong, and a great sense of humour as well as being deeply religious.

'Excuse me asking, Meir, how did you get into this type of business?'

He chuckled to himself and shook his head.

'It's a long story – one day I will tell you all about it.' For a moment, he lapsed into a hint of a different dialect. 'For now, let's get down to business.'

Chapter 34

We left Manchester on a total high. Meir had given us an order for three gross of willy-warmers. John said he would take over all of our remaining stock next weekend. I promised that the remainder of his order would be made up immediately and delivered as soon as possible.

The icing on the cake had come when Meir brought out a Father Christmas costume and asked if I was able to make them. He said that his usual supplier in Germany had increased their price, and the exchange rate between the Deutschmark and Sterling was making them unprofitable.

'Doesn't anyone in England make them?' I asked.

'Not yet,' he replied, raising his eyebrows and nodded his head as he handed it over.

We hardly spoke till we reached Belle Vue, both of us deep in concentration. John's attention was fixed on the road ahead; mine on the day's events, both of us stunned by the outcome of our visit. How were we going to complete this order we had committed to? I mentally calculated the amount of fabric we would require, and the sewing time. Where would we store them when they were finished? My stomach flipped – it was overwhelming.

'We could ask Bill if he would cut them for us.'

'He'll be too busy with his toys this time of year,' John replied.

'He'll not be using his cutting tables twenty-four hours a day. If he shows us how to use the cutter, couldn't we cut them ourselves? There's no harm in asking.'

We sat in silence again as we drove through Denton and into Hyde.

'My cousin Margaret can sew, she'd probably make some for us – I'll ring her when we get back.'

'I doubt if she's got an industrial machine though, or if she's even used one,' said John as he downed gears for the traffic lights.

Once again, Bill came to our aid and cut out the Santa suits. We also bought another used machine from him and placed it in Margaret's' spare bedroom, which she said would be her sewing room.

Her children, Sarah and Lee, were fascinated by the fact that their mum was making suits for Father Christmas, and told everyone at school.

'Why does he have to have so many?' asked Sarah.

'Because every time he goes down a chimney, he gets dirty and has to keep changing his clothes. He can't wash them with so many parcels to deliver.'

The run-up to Christmas came so fast we could hardly cope, but somehow we did. Even John and Dave learned to use an industrial machine and sewed and sewed and sewed. Poor Muffin, big and furry, was even more so with the amount of fluff forever in the air from the fur fabric.

The three of us rested for a few days over Christmas. After watching Mike Yarwood's Christmas Special and the best of Benny Hill, we finished the evening in the local pub.

We celebrated the New Year in The Captive Queen. As Big Ben's chimes rang out from the radio behind the bar, we joined hands with the regulars and the landlord and landlady for a noisy rendition of 'Auld Lang Syne', followed by a boisterous 'Hokey Cokey'.

We left the smoke-filled pub around one a.m. Loud music was coming from most of the dwellings on the estate as we began our short walk home.

'Hey, wanna come to a party?' someone called, holding a bottle and leaning against a door- frame. The door was open and the sound of Status Quo and 'Rockin' all over the World' filled the area. Children and adults were dancing around in party clothes.

'Happy New Year!' we called and waved as we passed. Muffin had been left over three hours and he wasn't used to being on his own for so long. *I'm going to get another dog, whatever John says*, I thought and braced myself against the cold east wind.

~

During the first few months of the New Year, the weather was bitterly cold, with snow, rain, sleet, ice and fog. John and Dave managed to get to and from work. For Dave, working and living on the same estate, it was no hardship. As for John, his journey took him almost twice as long. During bad weather, the seven hills of Sheffield were a nightmare. The long winter took its toll on my chest and I had Bronchitis again. John was concerned that it could be the fur fabric, but the doctors said not. The damage had already been caused by smoking from a young age.

Dave told us to take a holiday. He would look after Muffin as he worked nearby, and as the amount of sewing had now slowed down, he could manage.

I hated leaving both of them behind, but I needed the holiday. Another year lay ahead of us and working in the flat was becoming impossible. We decided to look for somewhere on our return.

We went to Corfu and stayed in a lovely hotel overlooking Mouse Island. For the time of year, the weather was beautiful. It had been a few years since John had ridden a motor bike; after looking at a map and seeing how small the island was, we decided to hire one and visit the different areas.

The roads weren't as good as they could have been, with potholes and dead-ends without signposts and roads that turned into farm land. We still enjoyed the adventure, laughing at every wrong turn, and the Grecian farmers, who shouted *tourists!* in their own language.

As we travelled, we noticed how green the island was, a landscape of woodlands, olive groves, imposing mountains, valleys and lakes. At Palaiokastritsa, with its beautiful long white beach and turquoise blue sea, we took photographs and lunched in a taverna, pulling faces as we tried the local Ouso.

Most days, we rode to a different resort: Kassiopi at the top of the island, a small fishing village, hardly changed with time, and then the climb to Pelekas, where we had a wonderful view of the island and took photographs of the lookout point called the Kaiser's Throne.

One of the most exciting parts of the holiday was walking along the causeway, which was a short-cut across an inlet, so that pedestrians could get to the other side of the island; vehicles had to go around via Corfu Town. The arriving and departing planes flew very low over the causeway; the sight and the deafening sound as the planes roared overhead was amazing.

Coming back on the bike from Glyfada one day, we were running late, having found a taverna where we had spent the afternoon trying to accustom ourselves to Ouso after lunching on Meze. The traffic was building up and the sun was going down.

'It'll take ages to get through Corfu Town,' said John, placing his right foot on the ground as we came to another halt.

'It's not usually as bad as this, there must have been an accident,' I replied, my shoulders burning as we sat waiting.

We waited five more minutes without moving.

'I'm going to take a shortcut across the causeway,' John said. He looked over his shoulder to see if there was anything coming from behind. There was nothing; only the stream of backed-up vehicles and anxious drivers.

'John, you can't. It's pedestrians only – it's not wide enough if anyone's walking across, don't risk it.'

He waited a while longer.

'We'll be here all night – I'm going for it, it'll be alright, hold on.'

'Don't, John, please…the steps.'

He revved the bike, looked over his shoulder again and pulled out.

Gripping my arms around him, he passed the stationary vehicles with sweating drivers slumped over their steering wheels. I was glad I

196

was on the bike and not roasting in a hot car. I closed my eyes as we approached the gap where the steps, partially covered with overgrown foliage, led down to the causeway. His arms flexed as he made the turn, I clung to him, and pressed my head to his back as he bounced the bike down the steps and onto the causeway.

We made it. The seat vibrated as the bike rumbled along the old stone cobbles.

'Wow!' I said as he began to make his way across. He slowed down slightly at the half-way point and then stopped, placing his right foot on the ground, the engine still running. I looked ahead to see why he'd stopped.

'John, you can't stop here,' I said. 'We're not supposed to be here.'

'There are some people coming across, I'll have to let them pass.'

'It'll be ages before they get here.' Thoughts of Grecian courts and prisons filled my head. 'But John…'

'Jack, I need to get a good run to get up the other side. I can't pass them riding this at the speed I need.'

I sat quiet and waited, afraid and yet excited. It reminded me of our hippy years, when we were younger and carefree. We lived for excitement and all the risks that came with it. As I sat waiting, I suddenly realised we were older. We had no children to remind us how old we were getting. I thought of the people I knew and how their offspring never allowed them to forget their age: *'Mum, you can't wear that. Dad, you can't do that. You're too old, you don't understand.'*

We had no one to please but ourselves.

It was getting darker as the group of people came nearer. I gulped as John manoeuvred the bike closer to the edge to allow them to pass.

I poked him in the back. 'That's near enough.'

The people gave us a ticking off; we couldn't understand their words, but their facial expressions and gestures made it quite obvious that we shouldn't be on the causeway.

John waited a minute until the people had passed and were away from the exhaust fumes. Releasing the clutch, he gave the bike full revs and set off on the short run towards the steps, steering the bike towards an old narrow water channel that ran alongside them.

Looking towards the top, I could see that this side was steeper and higher than the one we had come down. With a great jolt, the bike left the causeway and the wheels dug into the dusty earth. John raised his arms and body, lifting the front of the bike, his wrists twisting as his hands gripped the controls on the handlebars. I clung to him as he bounced up the channel and passed the first, second and third steps. Just as we came to the next, the front wheel caught the edge of the step, tilting the bike to the right. John tried to correct it but it swung wildly to the left and us with it, throwing us into the brambles and scrub lying alongside.

'Are you okay?' John said as he pulled me from the undergrowth.

I brushed myself down and shook my hair. 'Yes I think so.'

Stunned and shaken, we gave a sigh of relief and scrambled onto the steps. Apart from a few scratches, nothing was broken and we had no serious injuries. John righted the bike and between us, we managed to get it up to the top. He started the engine, switched on the lights, checked the tyres and tested the brakes and controls.

'Seems okay,' he said. 'Hop on, we've not far to go.'

~

The following morning, I was covered in mosquito bites, which must have happened when we fell into the bushes. By late afternoon, I was itching like mad, despite covering myself in the insect bite cream I had brought with me, which didn't seem to be having any effect.

We rode into Corfu town to find a chemist, who gave me some local cream. Twenty-four hours later, I had hardly slept during the night and the bumps had grown to the size of eggs. Feeling very poorly, we made our way back to the chemist, who took a good look at my bites and advised us to go to the local hospital.

We spoke to someone at the desk who couldn't speak English. She made a gesture for us to wait. The reception area was dull and hot; noisy fans turned above our heads, disturbing the warm air. After about ten minutes, a nurse came along; she also spoke very little English. She beckoned for us to follow her.

As we walked along the corridors, I couldn't help comparing the difference with our hospitals back home. We came to a stand-still. Speaking a combination of Greek and English, the nurse suggested that we needed to wait here. She stroked my arm and gave me a sympathetic smile as she looked at the massive bumps covering my exposed areas. As we waited in the dimly-lit, windowless corridor, where relatives held infusions of intravenous fluid bottles above patients' iron bedsteads, I felt ill and homesick.

John, unbitten, held me close and kissed the top of my head. The locals saw and smiled at us. I wondered what they would think if they were to see the inside of an English hospital. I began to cry.

Chapter 35

I was unwell for some time after arriving back home and it took ages for the lumps and swellings to go down. My rump was still sore, where an enormous needle had been pushed into it, along with another one in my thigh. No words had been spoken as the doctor attended to me; only the nurse who had taken us along the corridor. With hand gesticulations and a bottle of tablets, she told me to take them three times a day and go home to recover.

I was glad to see Dave and Muffin again, and we soon slipped back into our routine.

A few days later, John came in with some information regarding a bungalow for sale in High Green, a suburb on the north side of Sheffield. It looked interesting: a semi with two bedrooms, a lounge, kitchen, bathroom and a large garden, ripe for conversion. The owner, a widow, needed to go into full-time care.

'How much is it?' I asked.

'Eight and a half thousand,' he replied.

On the Saturday, John and I went to look at it. It was tucked away in a nice quiet spot and was near the park. The agent, after showing us the basics, sat in his car while we investigated it further.

'It's a bit small,' I said, stepping back inside the kitchen.

'I've been looking around the back – there's room for an extension. Here, look.' John pointed out the recess that would accommodate another room.

'What do you mean, have three bedrooms?'

'No, still have two – take out the stud wall between the kitchen and the bathroom to extend the kitchen and use the smaller bedroom as a bathroom.'

'What! Have just one bedroom?' I didn't like that idea.

'No, build another large bedroom in the recess at the back which I've shown you.'

'What about a work room for cutting and packing?'

'Got just the thing – a large Portakabin at work – no one uses it. I've already asked and I can have it if I pay Alan, the lorry driver for delivery. Dave and I can reassemble it and we'll get the lecky to run a cable from the house.'

I was more surprised at his comment regarding Dave than the fact that he'd thought the plan through.

I looked around.

'I like it, let's go back and tell Dave.'

Dave loved it and said it was a good buy. I managed to get the negotiator to accept just slightly less than eight thousand pounds. A small endowment mortgage was arranged and we used the same solicitor who had helped us to sell number twenty-six Tanfield Road. All we had to do now was to wait for a completion date.

~

We decided to complete as much of the work as possible while still living in the flat, especially getting the Portakabin into position so the cutting could continue. Although it was quiet during early spring, our willy-warmers were still selling and I had to be sure I had enough work to keep the out-workers busy.

We called in to see Mum and Dad on our way back from the bungalow. It was four in the afternoon and Mum was watching the wrestling on TV. She was also drunk.

'Where's Dad?'

'EEEeee! Give it him, get him!' she screamed and jumped up, raising her fists; her glazed eyes never leaving the screen as Mick MacManus floored Jackie Pallo. She sat back in the chair, bobbing up and down and beating her fists on her knees like a three year old.

I ran upstairs.

'Are you in there, Dad?' I tapped on the bathroom door. I heard him cough and turned towards the bedroom. 'What are you doing in bed, what's the matter?'

I went to his side and stroked his head. It was red hot and his breathing was raspy. I didn't like the look of him, he was ill and it looked serious.

'Dad – talk to me.' I took hold of his hand and helped him to sit up; he fell back against the pillow before I had time to adjust it. I looked around the room. 'Dad, are you taking any medicines?'

He suddenly recognized me and squeezed my hand.

'Don't let them take me in hospital, Jack, please…' His voice barely audible. He broke off and began coughing and crying, I passed him the bucket as he tried to turn onto his side.

'Dad, don't get up – here, use this.' I passed him a tissue from my pocket, and he spat into it. It was thick and dark, tinged with blood. He fell back, exhausted.

I heard John come back. He had gone to fetch a loaf from the baker's for me as none had been ready when I had called in earlier that morning.

'Up here, John. It's Dad, look at the state of him.'

John came upstairs; a look of despair on his face as he saw Dad.

'Here, hold his hand. I'll ring for the doctor.' I went downstairs, threw the soiled tissue in the bin and looked around for any medicine. Mum was still in the room, engrossed in the wrestling match.

Picking up my handbag, I went to the phone box at the top of the street. I phoned the locum doctor, then Dave; told him we would be late back and asked him to take Muffin out and give him his dinner.

'*Arsenal 3 – Manchester United 1.*' John Motson was reading the football results on *Grandstand* when I returned.

Mum, her energy spent, was now fast asleep. I went back upstairs to wait for the doctor while John went downstairs to listen to the rest of the results. Climbing onto the bed, I sat with my legs outstretched beside Dad and listened to his laboured breathing.

I was so glad I had stopped smoking. Looking at him, I saw an old man; he would be ninety next month. I stroked his forehead and tears trickled down my face. As I lay against him, I remembered the day Mum told me he wasn't my real dad, when I was ten years old. He had been my dad for six years before she told me, and when I knew, I was afraid of him not loving me as much as Jo and Ian.

My fears had been unfounded; he couldn't have loved me more if I had been his own flesh and blood.

I lay for some time, listening to the muted drone of John Motson's monotonous voice. Suddenly feeling cold, I sat up and pulled a blanket over me and saw my reflection in the dressing-table mirror. I remembered my wedding day and the photographer taking a picture of me and my bridesmaids looking into it. Our bouquets had been placed on the polished surface and reflected in the mirror.

Thirteen years had passed. I had left home, Jo had left, and Ian too. There was no welcoming dog here either. More tears fell as I waited for the doctor and I stroked Dad's forehead again, as everything within him began the process of closing down.

~

The district nurse came every day and I tried to visit at the same time. Between us, we managed to turn Dad and wash him.

John and I had moved into the bungalow, just four days earlier. However, I decided to stay with Dad, after arriving one day to find Mum trying to push a piece of pork pie into his mouth because he wasn't eating anything.

I lay in bed with him through his last night and listened to the rasping sounds from his worn-out lungs as his breathing lessened. Dad no longer knew us, and yet he knew I was there. I felt the grip of his hand in mine until the last few hours. Dad died at four a.m., on Monday 24th April.

John had come with me and was attempting to sleep in a wicker basket chair. Mum, oblivious, was snoring in the other bedroom.

'John. John.' I gently roused him from his non-sleep. 'He's gone – I'll go and make some tea.'

There was no point in telling Mum or anyone else at that time.

John followed me downstairs, where we sat silently drinking tea. After about an hour, I took a bowl of warm water, a flannel, soap and a towel from the bathroom and with John's help, managed to turn Dad's bony frame and wash him. I couldn't shave him; I'd tried before. His whiskers were too tough for his razor; I couldn't even manage it with the new razor John had bought. By six o'clock, he was washed and in clean pyjamas.

'I'll go and phone the doctor – he'll need to come and certify him,' I said as John changed into his work clothes.

'Okay,' he replied. 'I'll hang on here until you get back, then I'll have to get off.' We hugged each other and cried some more.

I rang the doctor, then Dave, who now had to journey into Sheffield to get to work, as he was staying at the bungalow with Muffin.

~

After the funeral, the bill had to be paid. Dad always said we would have no monetary worries after he died as he had ample insurance policies, which I knew he had by the amount of "Death-Hunters" calling on Friday evenings. What Dad hadn't realised was that he had outlived his insurance; the policies had been paid-up some twenty-odd years ago.

I looked through the policies with Jo. Ian said he would leave it to us – he couldn't contribute towards payment as he had another baby on the way. Jo then said the same, as their mortgage had just been increased.

I took out the policies from their long narrow buff envelopes. Liverpool Victoria: £15.10s; Refuge: £12.15s; Prudential: £26.12s. There were three more, giving us the grand total of £149.14s.5d. We had a difference of approximately £90 to find.

'Have you any money stashed, Mum?' I couldn't keep the sarcasm out of my voice.

'Don't be like that with her,' said Jo.

'Why not?' I snapped. Before I could continue, Mum snapped back.

'It's you with all the money, not me – flash cars, holidays abroad…'

'Huh! It's no thanks to you though, is it?'

Jo glanced towards me. 'I'll cash those policies for you, Jack, if you'll put the rest of the money to it.'

I glared at her. 'I'll bet you will.'

'What's that supposed to mean?'

'If you don't know, Jo, with your education, then I'm not going to tell you.' I got up to leave.

Chapter 36

After the funeral tea, Auntie Doris took me to one side.

'Don't be so hard on your mum, Jack-a-lee – she's had a hard life.'

'I know she has. I just can't stand her nastiness when she gets drunk.' I looked at her mousy-grey roots and realised that Auntie Doris was now old.

I looked around at other Aunties and Uncles. What had happened to their cheery laughter?

I know we were at a funeral, but after Granddad's internment when I'd been a teenager, my relations had seemed far happier than they did now. All our childhood days flashed through my mind. Uncles lifting kids up into the air and spinning them around; playing football in the park, the Whitsuntide walk when all the families and their offspring met up, when our cousins were our best friends, kids showing off in their new clothes, afraid of getting grass stains on them. Did any of this happen anymore?

'She was a lot younger than your dad, Jack-a-leen.' Auntie Doris brought me back to earth.

'Another drink, you two?' Uncle Eric cut in.

'You know better than to ask me, our Eric,' replied Auntie Doris and offered him a cigarette.

Uncle Eric declined.

'Has everybody stopped bar me?' Doris said as she lit the cigarette and immediately bent double with a raucous cough.

Uncle Eric shook his head, looked at me and gave me a hug.

'Your dad was a good man. He thought the world of his kids, including you – a damned hard worker too.'

'Thanks, Uncle Eric,' I sniffled. 'I'm fine with tea.' I gave him a peck on the cheek.

Auntie Doris recovered, after much gasping. 'Like I was saying,' she continued. 'She's a lot younger than your dad and he couldn't give her everything a younger woman needs.' She nudged me and nodded to make sure I knew what she was talking about. 'Sometimes, as good as a man can be, he doesn't always have what the woman wants.' She took a long drag on her cigarette, turned her head as she exhaled the smoke and gave me a sideways glance. 'How's your plumber friend, Dave?' She raised her eyebrows. 'Your mum knows about you and him.' She nodded her head once.

Auntie Doris certainly intended to make things clear. 'Give over – only thing Mum knows is where her next can of Gold Label is.'

'She's worried about John getting hurt, that's all.'

'She would be – she's always thought more about John than me. She just regrets having me – she could have had a good time if I hadn't been born.'

'Jack-a-leen.' Her tone changed. 'Your mother didn't have to have you.' Doris gave me one of her stern looks. 'A lot of women were pregnant at that time and a lot got shut. Your mother wouldn't hear of it.' She took another drag on her cigarette.

'I wonder who put that idea into her head.' I instantly regretted my words. 'I'm sorry, I didn't mean it to sound like that, Auntie Doris.'

'She was my sister, and the eldest of eight, and when our mum died, your mum was only thirteen, yet she brought us all up safely before she went into service. I would have done anything for her, anything at all.'

Tears filled my eyes. 'I'm sorry, I'm just being selfish.' I fished a tissue out of my pocket and wiped my eyes.

'No, you're not selfish, Jack-a-leen – you've had to play a similar role as your mother, and Jo and Ian had far more attention than you got as a child. You're just resentful, and who can blame you? I'll tell you this, all this has made you a strong woman – you're a born survivor. You'll have more out of life than any of our family has. The world's your oyster and it's yours for the taking, and believe me, you will. 'I'll tell you something else, if you don't become a millionaire before I die, I'll stop smoking.'

'Bloody hell, Doris, that's a big statement, I don't even do the pools.' I laughed. 'Come on, let's join the others before I pee myself laughing.'

~

I decided I would be more forgiving with Mum and promised myself I would see her more often.

Dave had progressed quite a lot during mine and John's absence. A stone fireplace had been built and a back boiler was installed to heat the central heating system he'd installed. He had also connected an immersion heater for use in the summer when the fire wouldn't be lit. A lot of work had gone into the bungalow and it was taking shape.

As I finished decorating the second bedroom and hung the curtains I had made, I suggested it would be better if Dave moved in temporarily as a lot of time was wasted while he travelled to and from Sheffield to go back to his flat, as well as for his day job.

John wasn't too keen. He didn't say anything and became moody for a while, before realizing we now had a garden to maintain, which John didn't want to be responsible for. Not that he disliked the garden; he just didn't want to do the work involved, whereas Dave loved it.

I loved it too, after living in the flat all those years with just a few patio plants and no grass, even though there was plenty in the park below. Muffin also enjoyed it: he sat outside, waiting for the milkman and the postman to come down the path towards the gate, and would then present them with a ball or a sodden knotted rope.

Time passed so quickly. John and Dave carried on with their day jobs and worked on the bungalow in the evenings and weekends. There was always a strained atmosphere between them; generally they worked well together and achieved a lot. By the end the summer, over half the work on the bungalow was completed and we sat back a little, reviewing what remaining work there was to complete and planning holidays for the following year.

One night in bed, I asked John if he was happy.

'Yes, why shouldn't I be?' We had made love and his arms were around me.

'Well…You know, with our arrangement.' My guilt never left me; it receded for a while, and always returned.

He pulled his arms away.

'Jack, what's there to say? It's all been said before.' He turned over and went to sleep.

~

John and Dave were at work and I was inside, doing the ironing. I could see Muffin through the window, sitting by the gate. He suddenly began barking and ran down the garden path. Putting down the iron, I stepped outside. He stood, wagging his rump at the bottom of the garden; something was annoying him. I went over and found a beautiful blonde-coloured ferret, equally annoyed with the barking dog. I grabbed it by the neck so it couldn't bite me and took it indoors, Muffin jumping up at me as we walked back up the path.

I'd never had a ferret before. When we'd lived in the flat, I'd had gerbils, hamsters, white mice, and lizards but drew the line at spiders, all belonging to my nephew Michael, who was John's sister Mary's son. He wasn't allowed to keep them in their flat, owing to Mary's asthma and as we lived nearby, he kept them in our flat and came to play with them most days after school. That was until he tired of them and I kept them for the rest of their natural lives.

Before the day was over, the ferret had been claimed by its rightful owner. I handed him over and asked where the lad lived in case the ferret decided to go walkabouts in future.

Muffin had been fascinated by his furry friend, and now we were no longer in the flat, I decided on another dog as a companion for him and for me as I had become quite broody. John wasn't too keen on the idea of another.

Chapter 37

We were doing well with our little business, just enough to keep going. It was demanding at times. I organized the cutting and sewing so the work was spread over the year and the outworkers had regular work.

I was vacuuming the carpet and singing along to 'Night Fever' by The Bee Gees, with Muffin attacking the monster that lived in the cupboard and was, with my assistance, challenging him. I finished vacuuming and as I was placing the monster back in the cupboard, much to Muffin's relief, the phone rang.

'Hello,' said a woman. 'Am I speaking to the person who makes the willy-warmers and costumes?' I didn't recognise her voice.

My heart began pounding in my chest. 'Yes,' I replied, as all sorts of notions ran through my head.

'Ahh, good! I've found you at last. You won't believe the difficulties I've had trying to locate you.'

'I'm sorry, I don't understand. What is it you're after?'

'You, my dear. I have a jokes and novelty wholesale company and would like you to supply me. I've seen the quality of your Father Christmas costumes and this is the quality I'm looking for.'

I stood in a trance, holding the phone to my ear, not knowing what to say.

'I'd like to come over to see your factory and arrange a deal. You're in Sheffield, I believe?'

I suddenly found my voice.

'Well, I'm afraid that won't be possible…I mean…can I ring you back please? You've called at a rather inconvenient time.'

'Yes, my name is Eileen, Eileen Wright. I'm the owner of the Fantasy Joke and Novelty Company in Leeds.'

I quickly jotted the information down and promised to ring her back. I sank into a chair and wondered what John and Dave would say when I told them.

While John and Dave changed out of their work clothes, I began telling them about the phone call. They followed me into the kitchen where I was cooking our evening meal. Muffin was waiting patiently for his.

'She thinks we've got a factory – how can she come here?'

'She takes us as she finds us,' Dave commented. 'What does it matter, as long as she gets her requirements?'

'Put some of that meat into Muffin's dish, please, Dave, I've already put the biscuits in,' I said, pointing to a dish of cooked leg beef.

'It doesn't look very professional though, does it?' I continued.

John leaned with his back against the opposite work top, his arms folded and tapping his chin with his finger.

'What about going to see her? She doesn't need samples – she already knows what we make.'

Dave placed Muffin's dish on the floor near the table.

'That's a thought, Jack. You could make a weekend of it. I'll look after Muffin.'

I placed the chips in the oven to keep warm while I flash-fried mine and Dave's steaks – John's was well-done and waiting in the oven. Yes, it was a great idea. I could visit the boutiques I used to go to – I wondered if Bus Stop was still there.

'A shopping trip. It's your birthday next month, Jack. Good idea.' John interrupted my thoughts.

'I wouldn't mind the trip to Leeds, but I'd sooner have another dog.'

We sat down at the table; Muffin underneath waiting for titbits.

~

We came back from Leeds with bags piled high with shopping. We'd bought Tina Turner's latest album for Dave. I had a new trouser suit: the jacket had fashionable wide shoulders and matching trousers; along with a pair of high platform shoes. John also had new shoes, and for Muffin and the new dog we would be getting soon, we bought some new pull-and-tug toys.

We also came back with a problem, a big problem. We could only just manage with the space we had for our current orders and now we had taken on another customer, another wholesaler with the same selling capacity as our wholesaler in Manchester. We spent the next few days deep in thought, hardly speaking to each other. This was something we hadn't expected.

We sat having our evening meals, talked in the pub, each of us proffering unsuitable suggestions as to how we would cope with all these extra orders.

'Another Portakabin in the garden?'

'Another extension to the bungalow?'

'Renting somewhere?'

'What if the bubble bursts and we're tied into a contract?'

After days of mulling it over, I was fully aware of the time schedule and decided that renting somewhere was the best option. I said I'd look into it, and when I did, it posed another problem. The units available to rent were enormous, terribly expensive and were only obtainable with five-year contracts. Now we were out of time, we decided to carry on and hope for the best.

'Now that's decided, let's go and get that other dog you promised me.'

'Jack, we haven't got room,' moaned John.

'Well, move out then if you want more space,' I said, laughing.

The Sheffield Star had adverts for lots of dogs that needed re-homing and I found an advert for another Old English at nine months old. Arrangements were made for us to go and look on the following Saturday. John and I travelled back to the Norfolk Park area where our flat had been. I looked up; the kingfisher-blue curtains

212

still hung in the windows. We drove past and up to the Arbourthorne district and found the house.

Candy was a gangly little dog with big brown eyes; she'd not taken on the gait of an Old English as yet, and she still had a puppy bark which was more of a yap. She made a fuss of the new visitors. Two young girls were playing with her.

'Stop it, Kimberley,' said the mother. 'You know you haven't got to play with Candy.'

Kimberley began to cry. 'It's not fair. Tammy can play with her, yet I can't.' She began to cry.

'This is why we have to sell the dog,' her mother said. 'Kimberley has asthma.'

'Aw, what a shame,' I replied and looked at John. 'Do you want us to take her and give her a good home?' I asked the little girl.

'No,' she snapped, and began crying again.

I felt awful and was in two minds whether to leave the dog here.

'She'll be okay.' The little girl's father spoke for the first time. He picked Kimberley up, placed her on his knee and whispered in her ear. The child went quiet, as if thinking something over. The other girl didn't seem to mind the fact that their dog would be leaving.

'Do you want her?' the mother mouthed. I nodded my head and she nodded towards the outer door. She quietly slipped the lead onto Candy's collar and led her into the hallway. The other girl followed, closing the living room door behind her.

John took fifty pounds from his wallet and handed it over; the woman passed me the end of Candy's lead.

'What about Kimberley?' I asked, feeling as if I were stealing the girl's precious toy.

'She'll be all right. Out of sight, out of mind.'

'Are you sure…?'

She edged us towards the door. 'Don't worry – we'll buy her another toy.'

'Not another dog, I hope.'

'No, no more of those.'

She closed the door behind us. A piercing scream came from the house as we made our way to the car.

~

'This is Emma,' I said, as I led her into the bungalow. 'She was originally called Candy, but I've changed it.'

Muffin and Dave took to her straight away. Muffin now had a playmate and loved running and playing with her in the park. She couldn't run and jump like Muffin with his rolling gait; it would come, in time.

Chapter 38

By Christmas, we knew our working conditions were impossible. We had less space now than we'd had in the flat. Every inch of space had been taken over with fabric or stock. With fur fabric, both the rolls and made-up items were cumbersome, taking up a large area. John and Dave fitted a pull-down ladder to utilize the loft space. However, our living conditions were still far from good.

Our new customer in Leeds, although she didn't get all her requirements, was delighted with what we could supply, and she understood our predicament; that I couldn't let my existing customers down as they had placed their orders earlier than she had.

After Eileen Wright had given us the projected orders from her company for the following year, we knew we needed more help. It was impossible to carry on as we were and we decided that Dave, who earned less than John, would give up work and help with the cutting. It was important that John remained at Tinsley Wire, as his wage guaranteed the mortgage. Although the business was now bringing in more money than Dave and I could earn if working elsewhere, I always had a niggling doubt about how long it would last.

I began to feel that I was taking on a huge responsibility, yet none of us had any knowledge of running a business. Somehow, I wasn't at all deterred. My whole being was filled with a buzz like I had felt when I'd first sat at Ellen Toulson's industrial sewing machine. I felt the throb of huge turbines that propelled the vast ships across the oceans. I felt empowered, and I sensed that this was just the beginning. The bubble wouldn't burst. I wouldn't let it.

'I'm going to night school,' I said. 'For business studies.'

John and Dave looked at me as if I'd said I was going to the moon.

'Well, don't look so surprised, you know how everything is getting out of hand. There's the second part of a course that started in September starting again in January over at Shirecliffe College. Dave can carry on with the cutting and packing and making sure Muffin and Emma get their regular walks. John can find us somewhere to work from.'

'Hang on a minute,' said John, throwing a shovelful of coal onto the fire. 'There isn't anywhere suitable, I've looked.'

'Well, look somewhere else then.'

~

At first, I thought most of the business studies course was just common sense, and I didn't stay the full term. I forged ahead, learning quickly and persuading the tutor to move onto the different aspects of business, thereby gaining a valuable insight into accounting and bookkeeping.

As each tutorial finished, I went home and pondered on the implications of what I had learned. I began to realise there was a lot more to it than I had thought, and if I was to be bookkeeping, accounting and corresponding, and doing stock control and sales, I couldn't also be making patterns and adjusting sizes. I would also need the services of an accountant for tax purposes. The business would also have to be registered. We were moving fast, on a treadmill of our own making, and it felt good.

'How do you fancy living at Penistone?' said John, one evening when he came in from work. He had shaken the snow off his coat and was removing his boots.

'Could you get the van in okay?' asked Dave who had cleared a path and a space for the van. He carried on feeding the dogs.

'Shut that door,' I shouted, nodding towards the living room, not wanting the cooking smells to permeate the rolls of fabric. 'Penistone, where the devil's that?' Interested, I put down the potato masher.

'You've seen it. It's on our way to Manchester,' John replied, sliding his feet into his carpet slippers.

'Don't tread the backs down. Why don't you wear mules?' I turned back to the stove.

'I don't like mules — why don't you stop biting your nails, anyhow what's for tea?'

It was a waste of time arguing and I wanted to know about Penistone. After plating up the beef casserole and dumplings, we sat down to eat.

'Come on then, tell me about Penistone. I can't remember seeing it.'

'We've not been through it…'

He began giving me directions to the place, totally confusing me.

'John, show me on a map after tea. Do you know where it is, Dave?'

'I've an idea — isn't it through Wortley and Thurgoland?' he replied, looking at John.

'Never mind all that,' I interrupted. 'What about it?'

Emma suddenly brought her dinner back up, depositing it at my feet. I pushed my chair back and patted her; she was ashamed of what she had done.

'Come here, poor baby.' I moved her away and fussed her. John and Dave stood up.

'You sit down, John and get your tea, I'll see to it,' said Dave, as he fetched an old newspaper to wrap it in.

I felt her head and her nose, they were both cool.

'I don't think it's anything much, she's perhaps got a chill,' I said as Dave wiped the floor with a floor cloth. 'I'll try her with a few biscuits later, that new meat might be too rich for her.'

We washed our hands and resumed our meal.

~

It was too dark to go in the evenings to look at the place John had seen, so we decided to have a look on the Saturday while it was daylight. Dave stayed at home with the dogs, saying it was mine and

John's decision, not his. I insisted that Dave was just as much involved as John and I; Dave still refused to come with us.

We didn't make an appointment with the agent as we only wanted to know if it had any potential.

'It's a long way from civilization,' I said, after going through Wortley and Thurgoland.

'It's not much further,' he said as we passed yet another field with snow at the edges.

'I'm not sure I want to live out here though, we're city folk.'

'We left the city when we moved to High Green, Jack. Besides it'll be better for the business…'

'Huh?'

'We'll be nearer to Manchester, Leeds and Bradford. It isn't as if we have people knocking on the door to buy things, is it?'

'I'm saying nothing till I've seen this place.' I folded my arms.

We carried on for what seemed like an eternity.

'Blimey, there must be as many fields out here as in America.'

'From here, it's less than thirty miles to Manchester and Leeds,' he said as he turned left and downhill.

'Yes, and about a hundred from Sheffield.'

'No it isn't,' he replied.

I suddenly saw a long row of arches with a train going across them.

'I remember now, from when we were children and travelled by train to Dad's relations in Crewe, Cheshire. It's coming back to me now. I'm sure we had to change trains at Penistone and Guide Bridge, wherever that is.'

The viaduct went out of view as we passed underneath and continued downhill.

'Is it me or does it feel cold here?'

John turned the heater up and turned left and we began climbing again.

'There's a short cut to where we are going…'

'I should hope so,' I interrupted.

'I wanted to have a look at the town centre,' he continued.

'This is a town? It's not as big as Chapeltown.'

There was an overlarge chemist to my left and a pub called The Spread Eagle to my right. He turned left; an old church was now on my left. I was surprised to see a cinema on my right, and it was showing the recently released film *The Shining*, starring Jack Nicholson. The council rates office was alongside.

John drove under another bridge, past another pub; at least there was no shortage of pubs. A large gritting lorry pulled out of a yard on our left; another one followed. John slowed to let them pass. The yard contained mountains of grit sand and a whole fleet of lorries.

'What's all the grit sand for?' I asked, as John waited to see if any more lorries were coming out.

'They keep the Woodhead Pass clear, and the main roads leading up to it.'

I knew where the Woodhead Pass was; we'd experienced enough long journeys over the moors to Manchester.

'Are we that near?'

'I told you it was on the way to Manchester,' he replied. He drove forward and then pulled into the side of the road and stopped. 'And he we are.' He pulled on the handbrake and turned the engine off.

'This is it? Wow!' I looked out of the window; on my left was a large stone house with a stone wall around it. The stonework had been blasted clean and looked like new. The stone pillars holding the large wrought iron gates had gold embossed lettering on, stating *The Queens* on both pillars.

I climbed out of the van and walked past the gate, John followed. A Rolls Royce was parked at the side of the garage. As I walked by, the garage doors were open. A chestnut horse was inside, feeding from a hay rack on the wall. This was even more bizarre. The voice of Kim Wilde singing 'Kids in America' came from an upstairs bedroom.

We walked to the end of the wall and turned down the steep street.

'John, its four storeys at the back and it looks like it has five bedrooms.' I suddenly realised what John had in mind. 'You're thinking of buying this and working from here, aren't you?'

'Well, as you keep saying, the bubble might burst – then it might not be a bad idea. We'll always be able to sell a house and move somewhere smaller.' We looked towards the bottom of the hill.

~

'Come on – let's have a look down there. This must be the River Don,' said John, as we stood on a wooden bridge that led to a cricket pitch. There was a path running alongside the river. A man came along with a spaniel at his heels, carrying a ball.

'Morning – pleasant enough, eh?' the man said.

'Excuse me,' I said to him. 'Is this the river Don?'

'Well if it's not the Amazon, it must be,' he said, laughing. He carried on walking, the dog following, tail wagging. He looked back and saw we were no threat to his toy and carried on.

We stood on the bridge, watching the river flow.

'Hey, look – you can see the viaduct from here. Do you think you can get to it along this path?'

'I should imagine so. Let's walk around the cricket pitch.'

We sat on a form at the opposite side.

'I could start playing cricket again if I lived here,' said John.

'I doubt it – you haven't played while I've know you. Quick, there – look.' I jumped up. 'It was a heron – it flew down into the river. Come on, let's have a look.' I ran across the cricket pitch towards the bridge.

'It's a good job it's out of season,' John shouted. 'The umpire would have you for that.'

I slowed as I neared the river; the heron's eyes were far too sharp and he took off from the water's edge, massive Jurassic wings lifting his long body off the ground and over the trees, following the river.

'Do you know something, John? I think the dogs would love it here.'

'Shall I ring the agent and make an appointment to view?'

'Not likely – we need to find out how much it is. I reckon it's out of our price range.' We walked back up the street.

'It's £29,500,' said John. 'It's been reduced from £39,000.'

'Wow, that's a lot. What do you think we'd get for the bungalow?'

'£15,000?'

'Give over, there's a lot of work and modernization gone into that. I'd have thought it was nearer the £20,000 mark.'

We turned the corner and were passing the gate, just as a young girl, about thirteen or fourteen years old, began to open it. She was leading the horse. John pushed the gate open for her.

'Do you want it closing?' he asked.

'No thanks,' she said, smiling. 'My dad's following me out. Whoa, steady on, Easter.' She patted the horse's neck.

The nearness of our van must have scared the horse. The girl held on to him with an expert hand. As small as she was, she had no problems handling the chestnut mount.

She led Easter away as a stocky chap came out of the house and began to walk towards the Rolls. He noticed us.

'Can I help?' he asked. 'Are you lost?'

'No, we're just passing…' John replied.

'Are you the owner?' I said, walking towards him.

'Yes, why, are you thinking of buying it?' He grinned.

'We'd love it, but I'm not sure we can afford it,' I said.

'Too big for most people, but you can never have enough room.'

'Why are you selling it, if you don't mind me asking?'

'Don't mind at all – there's not enough room.' He laughed. 'Come and have a look round,' he said. 'My name's Dennis, Dennis Tetley.' He put the car keys in his pocket.

'Jackie and John Creek,' I replied as we followed him into the house.

There was a doorway, leading from the garage into a utility room, where a large washing machine and tumble dryer stood. A massive utility table was fixed to the long wall, and a cloakroom and toilet was off to the right. We carried on down the hallway and into a large kitchen with a central workstation. A blonde-haired woman was mixing something in a bowl with two children watching on keenly, the younger of the two eating a jam sandwich.

'This is Linda, my wife, and two of the brood – Tracy and Cheryl.' He looked at Linda. 'This is Jackie and John Creek, Linda – they've come to buy the house.' He laughed again, a good-hearted belly laugh coming from a well-fed stomach.

Sensing that strangers had entered the house, a St. Bernard the size of a small horse waddled over and greeted us with slobbering licks to our hands.

'Stop it, Gemma.' Dennis stroked the dog's head affectionately. 'Soft as a brush, she is, aren't you?' He ruffled the fur on the top of her head. 'Have you got a dog?' He looked at me and John.

'Two,' I replied. 'Old English Sheepdogs.'

'You'll have room for plenty more when you move in here then.' He laughed again.

The youngest girl climbed down off the high stool, still holding tight to the sandwich. 'Are you going to buy our house?' she asked.

'Cheryl, don't be so cheeky.' Linda apologized to us.

Cheryl still wanted to chat.

'You can bring your dogs – what are their names?'

'Muffin and Emma, and they're nowhere near as big as your Gemma.'

She nodded her approval. 'We're going to live in another house with a big field at the side for Easter to play in.' She took another bite of the sandwich. 'And I'm learning to ride.'

'Come on, let me show you round,' said Dennis.

'Do you mind if I use your toilet before we start? It must be with coming in from the cold.'

'Cold? Cold? It's not cold yet, lass. You must be from Sheffield.' A wide grin spread across his face. 'It's over in the hallway, where you came in.'

I went to the toilet and couldn't believe I was standing in the home of someone who owned a Rolls Royce and a horse. They were just ordinary people, not at all like the company directors in the city, who lived at Fulwood and Dore.

As I left the toilet, a young man aged around fifteen, clutching a Sony Walkman the size of a small book bumped into me, the front of his blond hair flicked over to one side and falling over his forehead. I could hear Kim Wilde, still singing her heart out.

'Sorry,' he said. 'See you later, Mom,' he shouted as he passed by.

'Don't you be late back, Mark,' she replied.

We followed Dennis upstairs.

'We'll start in the attic,' he said, opening the door to the attic staircase.

The attic was huge; in fact, there were two rooms and the adjoining door had been removed.

There was an old settee, bean bags, odd chairs and stools, painted in a variety of colours, as were the walls. A Wurlitzer jukebox took up one corner and there was a set of drums in another.

A Barnsley football shirt, signed by Trevor Aylott, was pinned to the wall in one area, with a blue and white signed Sheffield Wednesday shirt framed on another wall. I could hardly make out the signature; then John confirmed it was Terry Curran.

'I thought he played for Sheffield United,' I said.

'No, you're thinking of Tony Currie, he's gone to Queen's Park Rangers. He went to your club, Leeds, before that. You should know – you're the Leeds supporter.'

'I haven't supported Leeds since Revie left and Clough took over and you know it.'

We carried on looking around the two attics, both large enough for bedrooms. Another corner held a home-made playhouse. This was a kids' paradise.

'This is the kids' playroom,' said Dennis. 'It's theirs to do as they wish, hence the diverse paint colours – they painted it themselves. They have their friends around and at least we know where they are.'

We turned to go downstairs just as Gemma was coming up, panting.

'Ahh, Gemma, we're coming down now.' We stepped to one side to let her pass. A big dog like her would have difficulty manoeuvring on the staircase. She reached the top, turned neatly and followed us down to the first floor.

There were five huge bedrooms and an enormous bathroom, with a tan coloured suite, with a bidet and also a corner bath which two people could sit comfortably.

'I'll leave you two to look around at your leisure – I'll be downstairs if you want anything.' He left us alone while we wandered amongst the huge bedrooms, my head swimming with ideas.

We joined him downstairs, Gemma following.

'Kettle's just boiled – tea, coffee?'

'Tea for me, please. Is it Tetley's by any chance?'

'Could be, I don't know – Linda does the shopping. I'd be expecting a discount for using my name if it is. We'll let that mash while I show you the rest of the place.'

Adjoining the kitchen was an open-plan dining room with a large window overlooking the cricket pitch and the fields beyond. A gas fire was at the far end and a small off-shot stood out from the external wall. Dennis explained it was where the hoist was, similar to a dumb waiter, for bringing the bottles upstairs from the cellar.

We went back into the kitchen and then into the front hall, which led to the upstairs. At the bottom of the stairs, a patterned glass door led into the lounge, which was massive. It had to be at least thirty foot by fifteen, with a large fireplace with a gas fire at one end and built-in glass-fronted display cabinets at the other end. There were two central heating radiators, on opposite walls from the huge windows. The room was tastefully carpeted and furnished, as were all the other rooms.

Dennis explained that the place had previously been a pub, and showed us how it used to be laid out. He had bought it from the brewery as a conversion project for his growing family, which had now served its purpose.

Having once been a pub, it was obvious that it would have cellars. They were the biggest and best surprise of all. This place was different: the cellar had its own stables. As an inn, horses had been housed here overnight, after coming over the Woodhead Pass, notorious for its bad weather, before they made their return journey. Of course, those days were long gone, although the history of the building was there to see, with old wrought iron hay feeders and tack hooks on the walls.

'Why don't you stable Easter down here instead of the garage?' I asked.

'We tried, but he didn't like it. I'll go and pour the tea – you come up when you're ready.'

John and I looked around the five cellars. 'This would be ideal, wouldn't it?' I said.

'Perfect,' John replied. 'It's all been rewired – all the cellars have an electric supply. The gas supply comes in here.' John pointed to the pipe. 'There's windows to the rear where the stable doors were – they've even been double glazed, there's access without going through the house, and there are drains.'

'I wish I'd never seen it, John, we'd never be able to afford this.'

'Come on, let's get that tea and apologize for taking his time.' Gemma followed us back up the stone steps.

'Help yourselves to milk and sugar,' said Dennis as we sat on the high stools around the central workstation.

The more I looked around, the more I loved the place. The kitchen was huge and fitted with modern oak units, a halogen hob and a built-in oven; a double-drainer sink with a large window looking over the rooftops of the houses below and onto the cricket pitch.

'How much is your gas and electric for a year, if you don't mind me asking?' said John.

'Not as much as you'd think,' Dennis replied and reached into a cupboard beneath the worktop. He opened a tin of biscuits. 'Help yourselves, you'll not find any chocolate ones left, Cheryl will have had them.' He pushed the tin towards us. 'The walls are two foot thick and it's double-glazed throughout with the new aluminium frames and depth for maximum heat saving.'

'That must have cost a fortune for a house this size.' I replied.

Dennis laughed. 'Not for me – *Radiant Superglaze* is my company.'

We talked at length about how he and his mate, both pipefitters, had set up the business a few years ago and now had their own factory. Dennis went on to say that the house would be perfect for us too, as we were just starting out in business.

I finally took the plunge and asked how much he wanted for the house.

'I've already reduced it by ten thousand for a quick sale as our other house is ready to move into. And it's on a bridging loan,' he added. 'If you've got a mortgage, you'll know how expensive that can be.'

'Ours is with Standard Life and it's fourteen per cent,' I replied. 'Anyhow, what are you asking now?'

'Twenty-nine and a half – can't do no better than that.'

'Thanks, Dennis. Can we go and think about it and come back tomorrow?'

'Sure,' he said, while John looked at me as if my skin had turned black.

We thanked him for the tea and promised to come back tomorrow at eleven o'clock. I couldn't wait to get home and tell Dave all about it.

John was annoyed and said I hadn't thought it through, and how were we going to raise the money?

'It's perfect for our needs with all that room – you know how much the rented units are. Look how many sewing machines we could get in the cellar. We wouldn't have to rely on outworkers – it would be much easier to manage. Plus, we wouldn't have to pay the extortionate rates like we're doing in Sheffield. We'll go back tomorrow and take Dave, let's see what he thinks.'

'Huh! Dave will agree with you whatever, and how are you going to explain who he is?'

The journey home seemed to take less than the outward journey. A note had been left on the kitchen table from Dave: *Took dogs in park, back around three.*

'I'm going to look for him and tell him all about it. Work some figures out for me while I'm gone.'

~

The following day, we went back, and as the gate was open, John drove in, off the road.

'Hello, again,' I said, as Dennis opened the door. 'This is my brother Dave, he lives with us.' The three of us entered; the two younger girls and the dog came to greet us. Gemma fell in love with Dave on sight, and wouldn't leave him alone.

'Give over, Gemma, stop it,' said Dennis. Gemma took no notice.

'It's alright, I don't mind,' said Dave and fussed her even more.

'I'll let you show your brother round – you know where everything is?'

I liked the fact that Dennis let us look around on own so we could talk in private. We took Dave around the house, following the same path as yesterday, pointing out features as we went: this would be ideal for that and that would be great for this. Dave took it all in, especially the cellars, where he could see the potential. We talked for a while; then went up the steps and into the kitchen. Linda was peeling potatoes by the sink.

'Tea, again?' asked Dennis as he placed some mugs on the worktop. 'Same for you, Dave?'

'Please – milk, no sugar.'

There were a few embarrassing moments of silence as no one wanted to be the first to speak.

'How soon would you need to complete?' I asked.

'That's another problem,' said Dennis. 'End of April.'

I put down the mug.

'That's only three weeks away and there's Easter in between.'

'We couldn't possibly do it,' said John.

'Hold on a minute.' I turned to face him. 'How do you know we can't? We haven't tried.'

We all sat, deep in thought.

'If you already have a mortgage, can't you extend it?' Linda said.

227

'I should imagine so, but we still have to sell the bungalow.'

We all went quiet again. I thought of the massive cellars and saw the machines in place and the sound of them running. I could hear music playing and machinists singing away as they steered the fabric through the heavy-duty machines. In my imagination, it was nearly Christmas and they were all wearing fur-trimmed Santa hats, tinsel wrapped around their thread stands, cards hung on lines beneath the shelves of boxes, holding brightly-coloured ribbons and lace, glancing through the window at the falling snow as their hands and feet worked in unison. Heaters on the walls blew warm air into the room.

'Will you take twenty five?' Everyone sat up. Linda dropped a potato in the sink. Gemma gave a low woof.

Dennis leaned back, John and Dave sat up.

'Look, Jackie, I'd love to take your offer and I know it would be ideal for your needs…' He stopped for a moment and rubbed his forehead. 'I tell you what – I'll split the difference with you – twenty seven and a half.'

I looked at John and then back at Dennis.

'Done.'

'Have you gone crazy?' said John, turning a whiter shade of pale. Then he looked at Dennis. 'Done,' he said, and held out his hand.

'For a quick completion,' we said, as we all shook hands.

'I'll ring our solicitor in the morning and get straight on with it.'

And that was it.

Chapter 39

The three of us sat in silence in the front of the van on our way home.

'I sometimes wonder about you, Jack,' said John.

'Oh, what's the matter now?'

'You know what the matter is – how are you going to pull this off? We can't possibly sell the bungalow and get the mortgage and solicitor and everything signed over in three weeks.'

'Don't be so negative. How do you know till you try? Anyhow, you agreed too. You go to work in the morning and leave it to me,' I said, sounding more confident than I was.

Dave didn't say a word.

~

The following morning, I arranged for an agent to come and value the house. I also phoned our solicitor, a new one, young and just starting out and probably wanting to make a name for himself.

He hummed and hawed and then agreed it wasn't impossible; that it could be done if everything else was in place. That was good enough for me.

I then phoned Standard Life and their response was similar. Yet, when pushed, they said it could be possible if all the boxes were ticked.

The agent came in the afternoon and valued the bungalow at £24-£25,000, which was much better than John had suggested. He wanted to take photographs and get it on the market, which he said would take a couple of weeks, perhaps a little longer, owing to the Easter holiday. I thanked him and told him I would talk to my husband when he came home from work and would be in touch accordingly.

I wrote out three postcards, advertising the bungalow for £22,500 for a quick sale, and placed one each in the High Green, Chapeltown and Grenoside post offices. I rang Standard Life and told them the valuation. Within the week, I had eight prospective buyers, although all of them had properties to sell or mortgages to get.

By Friday night, I was in despair. What had I done? Fear crept up my spine and through my body like icicles. Then the phone rang – someone wanted to look at the bungalow tomorrow morning. When morning came, I made sure the house looked as perfect as possible; everything to do with sewing was crammed into the Portakabin. John was putting a Saturday morning in at work and Dave took the dogs out for the due arrival time.

They were a youngish couple, probably in their late twenties. He introduced himself and his wife as Ryan and Janet Dawson. I showed them around the bungalow and told them to wander around by themselves. After surveying the living and sleeping areas, they looked around the garden and made their way towards the Portakabin.

I opened the kitchen door.

'Careful, in there, it's a bit cramped – that's why we're moving.' I shouted to them.

'Will you be leaving it?' He looked at the overhead cable.

'We'll have no need for it so, yes, if anyone wants it, or we'll remove it.' I went back into the kitchen.

After a while they tapped on the door and re-entered.

'Would you like any tea or coffee?' I asked.

They looked at each other.

'That would be lovely, thank you. Coffee please, milk, no sugar.'

'Same for me,' said Ryan.

We sat at the kitchen table and exchanged pleasantries. They were fascinated by my tale of why we needed to move and the business making willy-warmers.

'Well, I suppose we'd better get down to business,' said Ryan after the conversation began to dry up. 'We love it. Would you take £22,000?'

They had asked no questions about the rates or the running costs. He sensed my hesitation.

'Twenty two…' I repeated.

'It will be a cash purchase,' he continued. 'And we'd like to move in as soon as possible. We've just returned from working abroad and are living with Janet's parents at Grenoside, which isn't ideal.'

'What, living with Janet or her parents?'

He laughed and looked at his attractive wife, then back at me.

'If you can really go ahead straight away, I'll accept.'

Janet's eyes sparkled and she gave me a hug and they hugged each other. I felt overwhelmed with happiness for them. He shook my hand.

'Careful, that's my cutting hand.'

'Oops, sorry,' he said, laughing. 'Are you using an agent?'

'No, our solicitor is dealing with it. Look, are you sure you don't want to come back and have another look over the weekend?'

'No, it's perfect. I'll get my solicitor to give you a ring to confirm it's a cash sale, and that we both want a swift transaction.'

I sank onto the settee when they left and then jumped up and danced around the bungalow, singing *'Dance yourself dizzy when they boogaloo….'* at the top of my voice.

~

We had put so much effort into the bungalow and it did look wonderful. It would be sad to leave the place after just three short years. What was our alternative? They say everything happens for a reason. I was happy for the young couple who would enjoy their new life in such a lovely place.

All our hard work had not gone without just rewards; the higher price enabled us to move on and enjoy a new beginning. Who knew where that would take us?

In her younger days, Mum always used to say: 'Man plans, God decides.'

Although I wasn't religious, her words suddenly came back to me. Does one ever forget the indoctrinations of their parents?

What happens next?

If you enjoyed *The Power of Love*, you would love the concluding part of Jacqueline's life, *A Head for Business, a Heart for Fun*. Here's a short extract to whet your appetite.

A HEAD FOR BUSINESS, A HEART FOR FUN

1: 1997

'I'm afraid it's cancer,' the specialist said. We thought we had removed all the cells.

John and I sat frozen in our seats. We didn't even glance at each other; we continued to stare at the consultant as if he'd told us the world was ending. It was.

I wanted to stand up and shout and scream and strike him and the walls, and smash the glass in the window and jump out. But I didn't, I continued to sit and stare, unmoving. I was fifty-two, I wasn't even thinking about retiring let alone dying.

'Let me get you a cup of tea,' said the nurse who was sat by the side.

I should have known, why else would she have seated herself beside me. She quietly left the room. I thought of everything we'd worked for, all the years since leaving school at fifteen. What had been the point? A lump came in my throat. What about my dogs, John, Dave, the business, the staff, the house, who would look after them? No one would care for them like me. We were in the process of buying a penthouse in Tenerife; we were going to live there when retired. Jesus, this can't be happening.

The nurse returned carrying a tray; she placed it on the desk. 'Milk and sugar?' she asked while pouring tea from a teapot as if we were in a guest house. I listened to the stream of fluid pooling in the cup and the clock on the wall, ticking my life away, the only sounds in an otherwise silent room.

'Can anything be done?' I heard Johns voice, and the consultants reply.

'Although the cancer is quite invasive, we may still be able to stop any further spread; I think for now we need to concentrate on a full hysterectomy as soon as possible.'

I was now listening intently. 'When?'

'Within the next couple of weeks.'

'But it's my birthday, and we're going to Tenerife, we've some business to attend to.'

He rubbed his forehead, opened his mouth to speak and then changed his mind.

'I don't understand, what did I have done a few weeks ago?' I thought back to the colposcopy unit, where I was to have a biopsy. Laid back in a chair, my legs shaking on the padded supports, the nurse trying to comfort me with a hand on my shoulder. I was looking at the screen along with six students.

The doctor painted the neck of my cervix with the vinegar smelling liquid.

'We're looking for any dots of white that may show up.'

I cringed as the acid like substance stung and then knew it wasn't a good result when all the area turned white.

She picked up an instrument. 'I'm just going to take a small biopsy, Jacqueline. You'll only feel a tiny pinch.'

The area still painful stung again as she made the small incision.

'Ouch,' I could see blood and then a trickle; I flinched and cried, 'stop please.' The nurse gripped my shoulder.

The doctor had already stopped and bathed the area with a cotton swab.

'Sorry, Jacqueline, the area is too sensitive; it will have to be carried out under a general anaesthetic.'

My legs still in the stirrups and shaking like jelly. 'It hurts.' I said.

'Remain as you are for a few minutes until the bleeding stops and then we'll get you dressed.'

Another nurse came over with a sanitary pad and waited for the doctor to finish the task.

~

The consultant continued. 'The womb, ovaries and tubes, etc., are not exactly connected to other parts, such as the bowel.' He pulled a coloured diagram of the female anatomy from my file and pointed out where the locations of the different body parts located. Circles and arrows penned over certain areas. 'If we perform a TAH/BSO...'

'What's that?' I interrupted.

'Sorry, it's a Total hysterectomy with a bilateral salpingo-oophorectomy. Yes it is a bit of a mouthful, that's why we call it a TAH/BSO.'

'I'm sorry to interrupt, but I'm still no wiser, I know what a hysterectomy is, but I don't know what the other thing is.'

I took a drink of my tea while he explained. John was still holding my other hand.

'It's an operation we don't like to perform on a younger woman, but as you are now at a menopausal age...'

'I still have regular periods.'

He looked down at my notes. 'You're not planning on any more children are you?'

'No, I haven't had any.'

'Well then, am I right in saying you will not be in need of these parts. I do have to advise you that we cannot rule out the fact that it could already be affected. As of now, we cannot tell.'

'Will I have to have chemotherapy, radiotherapy?'

He opened his hands towards me as he spoke. 'That we don't know until we have removed the womb etc.'

For the first time, I looked at John. There were tears in his eyes. He was more upset than I, and concerned about what would it do to Dave.

*****

A Head for Business, a Heart for Fun, is coming soon. And don't forget, if you haven't already seen it, Jacqueline's first book in the trilogy, *The Girl with the Emerald Brooch* is available in all good bookshops. This wonderful tale, based on the writer's childhood and set in the industrial city of Sheffield, tells of a young girl unexpectedly having to look after her ailing mother, aged father, five year old sister and three-weeks old brother.

At this tender age when she should be playing with friends, she is coming to terms with birth and death. Then her mother shocks her by giving her an emerald brooch and telling her a secret.

You will be gripped from the first sentence as you meet Jacqueline's family and friends, and see how she turns into a rebellious teenager when she discovers boys, cigarettes, and rock 'n' roll, before facing the challenges of growing up and choosing her own path in life.

With dialogue reminiscent to the characterization of Catherine Cookson, and humour and pathos as found in 'The Full Monty' and 'Brassed Off', you will love this book.

If you want to read more of Jacqueline's remarkable life and quirky Yorkshire humour, she has a new book due to be released shortly and called **Poems, Prose and Tripe.**

This book as the title suggests, contains poems and verse – some pensive, some humorous - and flash fiction – which Jacqueline is also noted for. The book also has a narrative dotted with bits and bobs of sense, nonsense and her views on life.

Here's a taster.

POEMS, PROSE AND TRIPE

While recovering from my op, I began writing about my pets. In *Winter Fishing*, I give Barney a 'walk-on' part. But in Barney's case, it was more of a 'run-on/run-off' part.

Let me tell you about Barney. Barney was an Old English sheepdog, well he looked like one. White and grey, thick fluffy coat, floppy ears, and ambling gait, but that's where the similarity ended. He wasn't our first Old English, but he was our first seriously-uncontrollable-problem dog, and he was huge. Standing twenty-nine inches at the shoulder and when standing on his back legs, was as tall as I. Only two-years-old, he had lived in eight different homes and several kennels, in the hope of him finding a permanent home. All to no avail, no one could cope with him.

We collected him from the rescue centre in Welshpool, which is a long way from Penistone - even longer on a foggy day in late November. I no longer had my beautiful, gentle Muffin and knew I could never replace him, but we did have room for another dog, and my other two were both bitches. Living near to where we worked meant I could easily walk the dogs there and back, and they could remain with us throughout the day; each dog having its favourite place in the office, sewing room or shop and of course, the canteen. However, this lovely peaceful routine was now coming to an end.

~

We were late arriving at our destination in Welshpool, owing to the weather and getting stuck in a snow-covered ditch where we had to wait for a farmer with a tractor to come along and tow us out for £20. No mobile phones in those days and no phone boxes on country lanes in Wales. After meeting with the manager of the rescue centre and handing over £50 for Barney, we had to follow her to a farm a further twenty miles drive into the Welsh countryside to collect him. When we arrived at the farmhouse, the man had to fetch the dog from somewhere further afield, as it took another forty-minutes for him to collect the dog and return.

~

We sat waiting. The old farmhouse needed some serious repairs. The wife, I presume it was his wife, sat in a rocking chair near a coal fire, knitting. The only sounds were the ticking clock on the mantelpiece and the squeak of her chair. She slowly got up and drew the curtains.

'Fog's getting bad,' she said as she went back to the fireplace and gave the coals a poke.

My stomach turned over, it was getting dark, and we had a long way to go home.

I consoled myself with thoughts of the young dog desperately in need of a home and wondered if he would resemble Muffin in any way. I smiled to myself at the thoughts of a new dog in the house. I had been a long time getting over Muffin. Suddenly a loud scuffling noise came from the doorway and the door banged open. The farmer entered, struggling to contain the deafeningly loud barking beast he had on a chain.

~

I'll tell you more about Barney later; meanwhile, here's a poem I wrote after an incident while out walking with Barney. By the way, I'm not the fisher-person!

WINTER FISHING

I woke at dawn and drank a hasty cup of tea,
A good day for fishing I was sure it would be.
I packed some snap, my rod and some bait,
Wellies and keep-net – to get a good spot I couldn't be late.
With thoughts of Barbels, Chubbs and Bream
Put my tackle in the car and drove off down the street.

The river looked cold in the pale winter sun
Which made me shudder, and my feet turn numb.
I baited my hook and cast into the deep –
A fifteen-pound Barbel I was sure I would reap.
The hours rolled by as I dozed on the edge
But my float was still upright, so I threw in some bread …

Maggots and castor, but the fish still wouldn't bite,
Conditions were perfect with no one in sight.
No sooner said, than a woman appeared
Calling her dog which fell on deaf ears,
As he raced towards me with a great bounding gait
And clumsily plonked his front paws in my bait.

While I watched all my maggots wriggle into the ground
His slobbering chops my packed lunched he'd found.
'Barney – Come here boy.' But in vain she did call
As he gobbled up my pork pie, wrapper and all.
'I'm ever so sorry – he's still young and daft'
She called, pursuing Barney who'd got away fast.

Mayhem spurned I re-baited the line
With my one remaining maggot, and looked at the time,
The morning now gone, I shivered with cold
As the rod in my fingers, I barely could hold.

I placed it beside me and opened my flask. Mmmm,
Steaming hot soup, what more could I ask … A pork pie!
I smiled, warmed through with the broth.

Stomach now filled and spirits renewed
I settled back down for a good afternoon.
I dozed – still watching the bob of my float,
Suddenly sneezed, coughed, and felt a pain in my throat.
At half past three, the light began fading
No Roach, Chubb or Barbel, nor even a Grayling.

I reeled in my line; all it took was one look
At the one remaining maggot still skewered on the hook.
So I called it a day and packed up my things,
Yawned, and stretched out my cold aching limbs.
And stamping my feet, blew warm air on my hands,
My thoughts now of home and a steaming hot bath.

So, grasping my tackle and clutching dead grass clumps
I hauled myself up from the slippery mud bank …
Right into the path of a solitary walker –
Head bowed and tucked in averting the weather.
'Sorry.' I mumbled as drops rolled down my nose
'Caught owt?' he answered.
'Naa, just a flipping cold.'

Extracted from *Poems, Prose and Tripe,* available soon.
For more information visit my website:
http://jakc1wordpress.com/

 The Girl with the Emerald Brooch

The Power of Love
Poems, Prose and Tripe